An Introductory Guide to Scientific Visualization

R. A. Earnshaw
N. Wiseman

An Introductory Guide to Scientific Visualization

With 72 Figures

Springer-Verlag
Berlin Heidelberg New York
London Paris Tokyo
Hong Kong Barcelona
Budapest

Dr. Rae A. Earnshaw
Head of Computer Graphics
University of Leeds
Leeds LS2 9JT, U. K.

Norman Wiseman
NERC Computer Services
Kingsley Dunham Centre
Keyworth
Notts NG12 5GG, U. K.

Front cover plate shows an image of San Francisco with several multi-spectral analyses being carried out. Courtesy of Silicon Graphics Inc., AVIRIS data, and the Jet Propulsion Laboratory.

ISBN 3-540-54664-2 Springer-Verlag Berlin Heidelberg New York
ISBN 0-387-54664-2 Springer-Verlag New York Berlin Heidelberg

Library of Congress Cataloging-in-Publication Data
Earnshaw, Rae A. An introductory guide to scientific visualization/R.A. Earnshaw, N. Wiseman. p. cm. Includes bibliographical references and index.
ISBN 3-540-54664-2. – ISBN 0-387-54664-2
1. Science-Methodology.   2. Visualization–Data processing.   I. Wiseman, N. (Norman) II. Title. Q175.E233   1992   502.8–dc20   92-10987   CIP

Cover Design: H. Lopka, Ilvesheim
Typesetting: K + V Fotosatz GmbH, Beerfelden
33/3140-54321   - Printed on acid-free paper

Foreword

Visualization has been the cornerstone of scientific progress throughout history. Much of modern physics is the result of the superior abstract visualization abilities of a few brilliant men. Newton visualized the effect of gravitational force fields in three dimensional space acting on the center of mass. And Einstein visualized the geometric effects of objects in relative uniform and accelerated motion, with the speed of light a constant, time part of space, and acceleration indistinguishable from gravity. Virtually all comprehension in science, technology and even art calls on our ability to visualize. In fact, the ability to visualize is almost synonymous with understanding. We have all used the expression "I see" to mean "I understand".

Modern science part departs from the closed theories of the last century and demands computer simulations to understand real world situations. Scientific Visualization is the eyes through which these simulations are viewed, from electrochemical bonds to simulated interstellar jets associated with black holes.

Scientific Visualization is of value beyond strictly scientific applications, however. The same technology is now used in such diverse applications as clothing design, industrial design, automobile and airplane design, genetic engineering, chemical and drug design, oil and mineral exploration, chemical and nuclear power plant design, and motion picture special effects and animation. It is rapidly becoming a requirement for virtually all disciplines that deal with geometric things.

What is Scientific Visualization? It is a set of software tools coupled with a powerful 3D graphical computing environment that allows any geometric object or concept to be visualized by anyone. The software provides an easy to use interface for the user. The hardware must be able to manipulate complex, geometrically described, 3D environments in motion, color and with any level of "realism" called for to better communicate the essence of the computation.

Scientific Visualization is in its infancy, but the technology is sure to revolutionize scientific education. I believe that the requisite 3D graphical processing capability will be built into all personal computes within the next five years. And by the year 2000, I am confident that even the home digital television will combine such 3D graphical processing capability with digital video and audio. Then, even complex scientific textbooks will be viewed interactively on the home screen, with video clips depicting a lecturer, mathematical experiments run in and visualized on the "TV" and the student able to guide the learning process. But until then, such books as this will guide the way.

May 1992   James H. Clark
                                Chairman, Silicon Graphics Inc
                                Mountain View
                                California, USA

Preface

Scientific visualization is concerned with exploring data and information in such a way as to gain understanding and insight into the data. This is a fundamental objective of much scientific investigation. To achieve this goal, scientific visualization involves aspects in the areas of computer graphics, user-interface methodology, image processing, system design, and signal processing.

This guide is intended for readers new to the field who require a quick and easy-to-read summary of what scientific visualization is and what it can do. Written in a popular and journalistic style with many illustrations, it will enable readers to appreciate the benefits of scientific visualization and how current tools can be exploited in many application areas. It will be invaluable for scientists and research workers who have never used computer graphics or other visual tools before, and who wish to find out the benefits and advantages of the new approaches.

This guide is concerned to answer the questions which the newcomer to visualization may wish to ask concerning what it is, what it can do, what facilities are available, and how much it costs. Points of contact for further information are also provided.

About the Authors

Dr. R.A. Earnshaw
University of Leeds
UK

Rae Earnshaw is Head of Computer Graphics at the University of Leeds, with interests in graphics algorithms, scientific visualization, display technology, CAD/CAM, and human-computer interface issues. He has been a Visiting Professor at Illinois Institute of Technology, Chicago, USA, Northwestern Polytechnical University, China, and George Washington University, Washington DC, USA. He was a Director of the NATO Advanced Study Institute on "Fundamental Algorithms for Computer Graphics" held in Italy, England, in 1985, a Co-Chair of the BCS/ACM International Summer Institute on "State of the Art in Computer Graphics" held in Scotland in 1986, and a Director of of the NATO Advanced Study Institute on "Theoretical Foundations of Computer Graphics and CAD" held in Italy in 1987. He is a member of ACM, IEEE, CGS, EG, and a Fellow of the British Computer Society.

Mr. Norman
Wiseman
Natural Environment Research
Council, UK

Norman Wiseman is Northern Area Computer Services Manager for the Natural Environment Research Council. His special interests are in the application of visualization in physical and biological sciences of the environment; education and training of scientists in the use of graphical techniques; and raster print technology. He has been a systems consultant for a number of years and has been involved in several graphics hardware, software and training initiatives in the UK Academic and Research Council communities. Prior to this he has worked on a number of software projects involving the acquisition, storage, display and analysis of seismic and borehole log data, primarily for use by scientists in the British Geological Survey. He is a member of Eurographics.

Contents

Part II   Overview of Current Systems and Developments

Acknowledgements

Phil Andrews (Pittsburgh Supercomputer Center), Mike Bundred (UNIRAS Ltd.), Tat-Seng Chua (National University of Singapore), D. Scott Dyer (Ohio Supercomputer Center), Basem El-Haddadeh (University of Leeds), Todd Elvins (San Diego Supercomputer Center), Mark Goossens (Silicon Graphics Ltd.), Chris Green (British Geological Survey), Simon Hansford (Precision Visuals), Dee Holmes (Stardent Computer Ltd.), Peter Irwin (Dynamic Graphics Ltd.), Teruaki Ito (Ricoh Company Ltd.), Tosiyasu L. Kunii (University of Tokyo), Hideko S. Kunii (Ricoh Company Ltd.), Chris Little (Meteorological Office), Donna McMillan (Sun Microsystems Inc.), Nadia Magnenat-Thalmann (University of Geneva), Eihachiro Nakamae (Hiroshima University), Gordon Oliver (LightWork Design Ltd.), Aidan O'Neill (Ricoh Company Ltd.), Peter Quarendon (IBM UK Scientific Centre), John Rasure (University of New Mexico), David F. Rogers (US Naval Academy), Peter Stothart (Wavefront Technologies Ltd.), Yasuhito Suenaga (NTT Human Interface Laboratories), Daniel Thalmann (Swiss Federal Institute of Technology), Hiroshi Toriya (Ricoh Company Ltd.), Craig Upson (Silicon Graphics Inc.), Joel Welling (Pittsburgh Supercomputer Center), Jane Wheelwright (Dynamic Graphics Ltd.), Michael Wood (University of Aberdeen), Brian Wyvill (University of Calgary), Geoff Wyvill (University of Otago).

Many people have supplied information on their uses and applications of visualization systems. Many designers and implementors have supplied details of their systems and also illustrations. Others have supplied details of aspects of visualization, as well as slides. We express our thanks and appreciation to:

The contributions of members of the the AGOCG Workshop on Scientific Visualization held in the UK, 22–25 February 1991, are gratefully acknowledged. We particularly appreciated the comments of the following on a first draft of this guide: Ken Brodlie, Lesley Carpenter, Kate Crennell, Todd Elvins, Hilary Hearnshaw, Roger Hubbold, Chris Little, Anne Mumford, Howard Watkins, and Mike Wood. However, responsibility for the final text remains with the authors.

Some companies were unable to supply information or illustrations of their products, despite being invited to do so. They have therefore been omitted from the information on current vendor systems. The list of vendor systems is not therefore claimed to cover all the systems in the market place at the time of writing. Those that are covered are the ones where information was obtainable.

Disclaimer

We are indebted to the following for the use of copyright material and illustrations: The views expressed by the contributors of information on products is believed to be accurate and given in good faith. However, authors and publisher do not hold themselves responsible for the views expressed in this volume in connection with vendor products or public domain products. In addition, the authors and publisher do not hold themselves responsible for the accuracy or otherwise of data extracted from vendor specifications.

Copyright Material

Chris Little, UK Meterological Office (UK Government), Peter Quarendon, IBM UK Scientific Centre, David F. Rogers, US Naval Academy, Regional Geophysics Research Group, British Geological Survey, Peter Stothart, Wavefront Technologies Ltd., Mike Bundred, UNIRAS Ltd., Precision Visuals Ltd., Stardent Computer Ltd., Silicon Graphics Inc., Spyglass Inc., Ricoh Company Ltd., San Diego Supercomputer Center, Donna McMillan, Sun Microsystems Inc., Gordon Oliver, LightWork Design Ltd., Nadia Magnenat-Thalmann, University of Geneva, Daniel Thalmann, Swiss Federal Institute of Technology.

Trademarks

UNIX is a trademark of AT & T Inc., OPEN LOOK is a trademark of AT & T Inc., X Window is a trademark of Massachusetts Institute of Technology, X11 is a trademark of Massachusetts Institute of Technology, Motif is a trademark of the Open Software Foundation Inc., PostScript is a registered trademark of Adobe Systems Inc., Ethernet is a trademark of Xerox Corporation, MS-DOS is a trademark of Microsoft Corporation, Stardent is a trademark of Stardent Computer Inc., AVS is a trademark of Stardent Computer Inc., DORE is a trademark of Stardent Computer Inc., Silicon Graphics is registered trademark of Silicon Graphics Inc., IRIS is a registered trademark of Silicon Graphics Inc., POWER series is a trademark of Silicon Graphics Inc., Graphics Library is a trademark of Silicon Graphics Inc., Image Vision Library is a trademark of Silicon Graphics Inc., IL is a trademark of Silicon Graphics Inc., GL is a trademark of Silicon Graphics Inc., Live Video Digitizer is a trademark of Silicon Graphics Inc., StereoView is a trademark of Silicon Graphics Inc., Explorer is a trademark of Silicon Graphics Inc.., Personal Visualizer is a trademark of Wavefront Technologies Inc., Data Visualizer is a trademark of Wavefront Technologies Inc., Advanced Visualizer is a trademark of Wavefront Technologies Inc., SunVision is a trademark of Sun Microsystems Inc., Sun-View is a registered trademark of Sun Microsystems, Open-Windows is a trademark of Sun Microsystems Inc., XDR is a trademark of Sun Microsystems Inc., XGL is a trademark of Sun Microsystems Inc., SPARC is a registered trademark of SPARC International Inc., SPARCstation is a trademark of SPARC International Inc., IBM, PC, PS/2 are trademarks of IBM Corporation, PV-WAVE is a trademark of Precision Visuals Inc., NAG is a registered trademark of Numerical Algorithms Group Ltd. and, Numerical Algorithms Group, Inc., RenderMan is a registered trademark of PIXAR, RIB is a trademark of Pixar, Spyglass is a trademark of Spyglass Inc., MacIntosh is a trademark of Apple Computer Inc.,

This is an aggregated list of registered trademarks and trademarks used in the volume. In order to identify products unambiguously it is necessary to use these terms. The following are known to be trademarks or registered trademarks of the companies concerned. We trust that others that may not be noted are known to readers and are referenced in a manner acceptable to the companies concerned.

Laserwriter is a trademark of Apple Computer Inc., LightWorks is a trademark of LightWork Design Ltd., NeXT Cube is a trademark of NeXT Computers, SpaceBall is a trademark of Spatial Systems Inc., DataGlove is a trademark of VPL, 3D Polhemus Digitizer is a trademark of Polhemus, EyePhone is a trademark of VPL Research Inc., VoxelView is a trademark of Vital Images Inc., VoxelLab is a trademark of Vital Images Inc.

Part I

Basics of
Scientific
Visualization

Chapter 1
Introduction and Background

1.1 Introduction

This guide seeks to answer the following questions:

- What is scientific visualization?
- What can it do?
- What do the technical terms and the jargon really mean?
- What products are currently available?
- What kind of hardware do I need?
- What are the costs?
- What do I get?
- Where do I go next to find out more, or to explore current possibilities?
- What are the prospects for the future?

The first part of this volume is concerned with introducing the topic, definitions, terminology, techniques, methodology, and equipment. The second part contains an overview of current systems and developments.

1.2 Background

The area encompassed by scientific visualization is defined in this guide, with the range of possible applications, and the potential for the future. Considerable advances have been made in the USA by dissemination of information and by coordinated initiatives from industry and professional organisations such as the Association for Computing Machinery (ACM).

Information

Objectives   The objective of this guide is to inform the general reader about scientific visualization, what it offers, and what it can do. It should be useful to scientists and engineers who are not specialists in computing matters, but nonetheless wish to use effective computer-based tools to further research objectives.

Developments and initiatives in the USA are summarized. These demonstrate the relevance and importance of scientific visualization.

Facilities   Software products are outlined and summarised – for purposes of general information. These are indicative of the kind of products available in the market place, and that are supported on a variety of platforms. However, this is not intended to be exhaustive, and in certain application areas a wide variety of software has been developed.

Current developments in animation are summarized because it is likely to become increasingly important for scientific visualization.

Summary   This guide provides an overall summary of the benefits that accrue from scientific visualization and the methods, tools and strategies that comprise its domain.

Chapter 2
What Scientific Visualization Can Do!

2.1 What is Scientific Visualization?

"The purpose of computing is insight, not numbers" wrote *Insight not*
the much-cited Richard Hamming in *Numerical Methods for* *numbers*
Scientists and Engineers (McGraw-Hill, 1962). Scientific visualization is an amalgam of tools and techniques that seeks
to promote new dimensions of insight into problem-solving
using current technology.

Scientific visualization is concerned with exploring data *What is it?*
and information graphically – as a means of gaining understanding and insight into the data. Scientific visualization is
a graphical process analogous to numerical analysis, and is
often referred to as visual data analysis. Scientific visualization systems are combinations of hardware and software systems and techniques.

By displaying multi-dimensional data in an easily under- *Multidimensional*
standable form on a 2D screen, it enables insights into 3D
and higher-dimensional data and data sets that were not formerly possible.

Often data sets are very large, and this gives rise to prob- *Large volumes*
lems of scale and of finding correlations and relationships
between different parts of the data.

Visualization is also a means of gaining a quick under- *Speed*
standing of processes. This could be done in more classical
ways, but might take much longer.

The difference between scientific visualization and pre- *Not presentation*
sentation graphics is that the latter is primarily concerned *graphics*
with the communication of information and results that are
already understood. In scientific visualization we are seeking to *understand* the data.

Lots of tools   Visualization involves aspects in the areas of computer graphics, user interface, cognitive science, image processing, design, and signal processing. Formerly these were independent fields, but convergence is being brought about by the use of analogous techniques in the different areas. Visualization is thus an additional tool for scientific research and investigation.

Help for   Visualization highlights applications and application areas because it is concerned with providing the means for a user to achieve greater exploitation of computing tools now available. In a number of instances visualization has been used to analyze and display large volumes of multi-dimensional data in such a way as to allow the user to extract significant features and results quickly and easily. Tools and techniques in this area are therefore concerned with data analysis and data display, perhaps with provision for the display of data changes with respect to time.

Examples   Non-destructive and non-invasive examination of the internal structures of living organisms (e.g., reconstructions from brain scan data), turbulence effects in fluid flow, and genetic engineering are all examples that have caught the public attention, and where scientific visualization has brought substantial benefits. However, this is but one aspect of the whole field, as indicated above.

Simulating nature   Visualization fits into the overall process of numerical simulation as indicated in Figure 2.1 below.

In the computational sciences the main goal is to understand the workings of nature. In order to accomplish this, the scientist proceeds through a number of steps from observing a natural event or phenomena to analyzing the results of a simulation of the phenomena. Visual representation of this data is often indispensible in gaining an understanding of the processes involved.

Interactive steering   Visualization systems can be used for the interactive steering of computations. The user observes the progress of the computation visually and alters parameter values accordingly. These in turn determine the future computation.

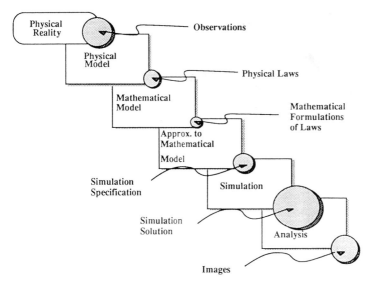

Physical Reality — Physical Model — Observations

Physical Model — Physical Laws

Mathematical Model — Mathematical Formulations of Laws

Approx. to Mathematical Model

Simulation Specification — Simulation

Simulation Solution — Analysis

Images

Fig. 2.1
Simulating Nature.
Simulating natural
phenomena: the
boxes represent
processes, the
circle's size
indicates the
relative volume of
information
passing between
each pair of
processes

2.2 How to do Scientific Visualization

Visualization tools benefit from the availability of modern workstations with good performance, large amounts of memory and disk, and with powerful graphics facilities – in terms of range of colors available, resolution, and speed of display by the workstation. This close coupling of graphics and raw computation power is a powerful combination for those areas where visual insight is an important part of the problem-solving capability.

Computing power

Such workstations now offer substantial computation power coupled with high-speed 3D graphics. These facilities can be exploited to significant advantage in application areas such as modeling, simulation, and animation. Real-time dynamical simulation can involve the processing and display of large amounts of data, and often the only effective analysis of the performance or validity of the model is through visual observation.

3 dimensions

Leading-edge applications will tend to require the most powerful systems available. The vendors listed later in this volume provide a range of systems to match a wide variety of applications, and are continuously improving computation power and graphics capabilities.

Supercomputers   Such workstations provide the computation power to process the data, and the high-speed graphics pipeline can transform this into graphical images, often in real time. In those cases where additional computational resources are required, the calculation can be off-loaded onto a supercomputer, or other advanced workstations with spare capacity, and the resulting image down-loaded for viewing (and perhaps even interaction) when it is ready.

Output   Output is often most useful as information on the workstation screen, especially when the process is interactive. More permanent copies of screen images can be printed in full color on A4 to A0 plotters and printers and on video or slides. However, this requires additional hardware and software. Generally, the higher the cost the greater the variety of colors and quality of the final images.

2.3 Some Examples of Scientific Visualization

2.3.1 The March of Napoleon's Army

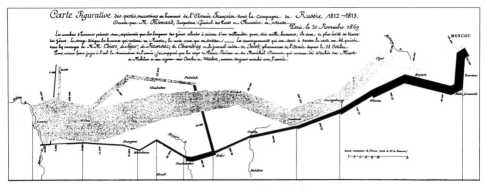

Fig. 2.2   March of Napoleon's Army

The classic map/chart of Napoleon's march in Russia, and the retreat of 1812, drawn by Charles Joseph Minard.

This is a good example of visualization which clearly pre-dates scientific visualization!

2.3.2 Cholera Outbreak

The work of Dr. John Snow (Gilbert 1958) provides an early example of cartographic visualization in problem analysis. While investigating the 1853–54 cholera outbreak in London he identified what he called a "cholera-field" in the Soho area. He had plotted the homes of the 500 victims who had died in the first 10 days of September 1854 and this simple visualization (of quite a large and complex data set) drew his attention to the previously unsuspected link between water supply and the disease. All victims had drunk from the Broad Street pump, in the middle of the "field",

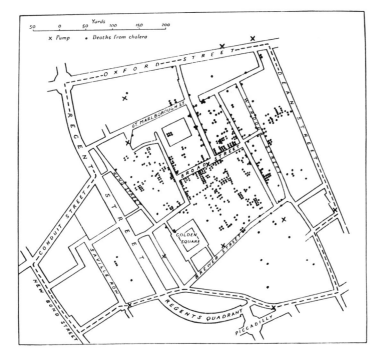

Fig. 2.3
Dr. John Snow's
map (1855) of
deaths from
cholera in the
Broad Street area
of London in
September 1854

which, it was later established, was being polluted by a leaking cesspool. The "link" was confirmed by noting that a virtually disease-free area (a large workhouse) within this zone had its own clean water supply.

2.3.3 Weather Maps from Meteorology

The following three maps illustrate various aspects of weather patterns.

This first map (Figure 2.4) shows the raw numerical forecast data with contour lines showing the pressure. This is a distillation of the information contained in thousands of numbers! The second map (Figure 2.5) shows where the fronts have been positioned. This is an interpretation of the above map, and presents the data in a form that people can understand more easily. The third map (Figure 2.6) shows a tailored short-hand form of the second map, and is the kind used by aircraft pilots.

Fig. 2.4
Weather Map 1

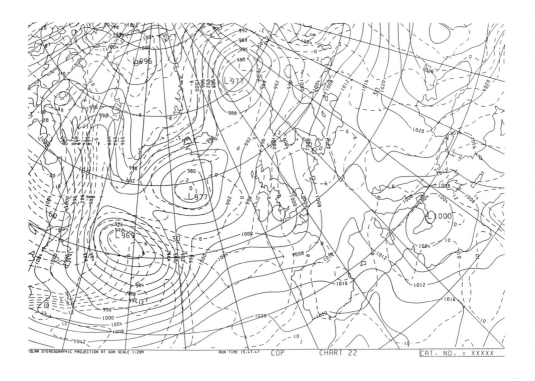

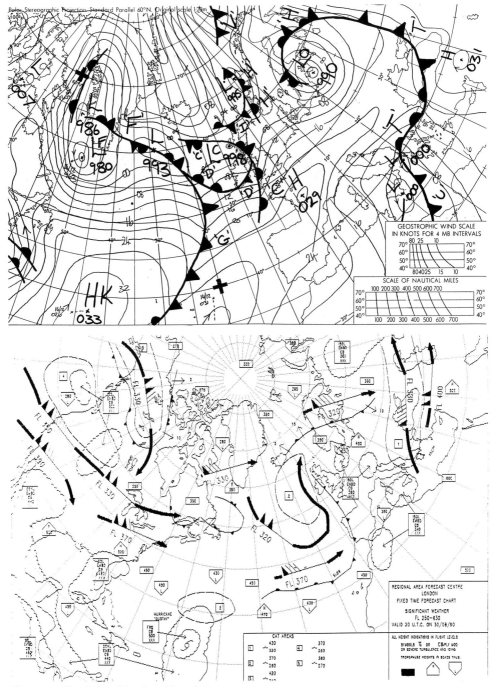

Above: Fig. 2.5   Weather Map 2

Below: Fig. 2.6   Weather Map 3

2.3.4 Molecular Modeling

This example shows a molecular model of liver alcohol de-
hydrogenase – calculated by computer and then displayed.
The mauve molecule fitting into the enzyme shows the
structure of the underlying molecule.

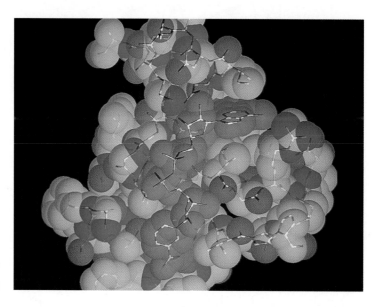

Fig. 2.7
Molecular Model

2.3.5 Pelvic Reconstruction

Karen Frankel
(1989) reported the
following case

A young man in his late twenties suffered a crushed pelvis
in an auto accident. His orthopedists said that the fracture
was too complicated to operate on and elected to treat him
conservatively; he would be in traction for a few months.
The doctors were certain that the young man would be per-
manently crippled.

Luckily the man's father, also a physician, knew of research in 3D rendering of computed tomography (CT) scan
data. He sent his son's CT scan studies to the researchers,
a radiologist, and orthopaedic surgeon, and a computer
graphics expert, who studied the volumetric rendering of
the pelvis that was created with specially designed hardware

and software. Able to see it from all angles, they determined the extent of the fracture and locations of several key fragments. The pelvis was operable and the next day the surgeons set the fragments. Three months later the patient returned for a check up and demonstrated full-range hip motion.

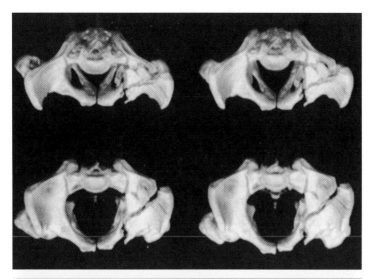

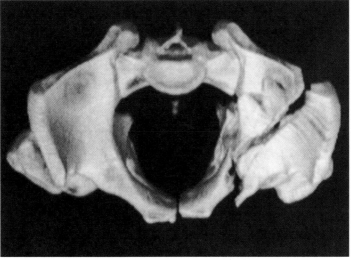

Fig. 2.8 Fractured Pelvis. Volume renderings of the broken pelvis using CT scan data by Professor Elliot K. Fishman of Johns Hopkins University Hospital, Dept of Radiology. The extent of the fracture and location of the fragments are clearly visible. Although radiologists have been using CT data for almost 20 years, volume renderings of CT offer a new way of interpreting such data

This case coupled great medicine and great computer science. The technique of volume rendering changed the course of treatment by providing the physicians with more data. This data ultimately gave them the confidence to operate and thereby improve the patient's quality of life. While volume rendering helped manage the medical complexities, this case also represents departures from tradition for both disciplines.

Text: courtesy of ACM

2.3.6 Oil Exploration

This example shows the use of visualization in oil exploration. The volumetric data was produced as part of a simulation of a method for recovering oil from the tar sands of northern Alberta, Canada.

This process was simulated by the Alberta Oil Sands Technology Research Authority and the visualization was computed by Geoff Wyvill and Brian Wyvill.

Courtesy of Geoff Wyvill and Brian Wyvill.

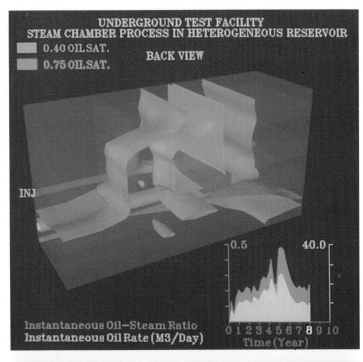

*Fig. 2.9
Oil Explora-
tion 1.
Iso-temperature
contour surfaces
from Volumetric
Data produced by
simulation. The
surfaces are tiled
using the "Soft
Object" algorithm.
The red pipe
represents the
"injection well"
which pumps
superheated
steam into the
rocks*

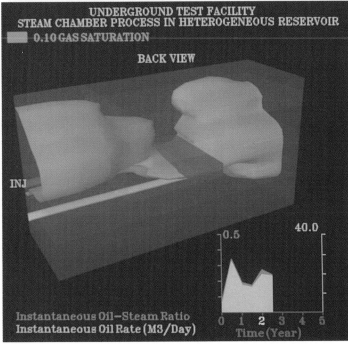

*Fig. 2.10
Oil Explora-
tion 2.
As the simulation
progresses the
surface changes
shape as the
rocks are heated.
After a period of
time, oil is
precipitated into
the production
pipe*

2.3.7 Designing Ship Propellors
Sculptured Surface Fitting and Fairing

Shape design

The fairness of a sculptured surface is important for design applications as diverse as modern artistic sculptures and aircraft or automobiles. The requirement for fairness can be based on either aesthetic or technical considerations. Currently there is no universally accepted mathematical definition of fairness. One technique that aids in evaluating surface fairness is to look at the Gaussian curvature of the surface.

Visualizing the surface

The Gaussian curvature of a surface is visualized by using the values of Gaussian curvature to color encode the surface. If the surface is fair, then the color hue smoothly transitions across the surface. Unfairnesses show up as splotches or lines of color within the surface.

The three accompanying images show one side of the surface and the fillet for a single blade of a ship propeller. The data supplied by the designer is shown in Fig. 2.11 visualized with a dynamic three-dimensional rational B-spline surface design program called Rbssd developed by Professor David F. Rogers.

The data set is a combination of two independent data sets comprising the surface and the fillet. Visualized in this way it is obvious that the lines of data for the fillet and the surface are not aligned. This has implications when a rational B-spline surface is fit to the data.

Figure 2.12 shows the rational B-spline surface generated by the defining polygon net. The surface appears reasonably smooth.

Figure 2.13 illustrates the color coded Gaussian curvature surface. This shows that the surface is unfair. Here the green indicates zero Gaussian curvature and the yellow positive Gaussian curvature. The areas of yellow indicate ridges or bumps or hollows in the otherwise developable surface. Notice that many of these are concentrated in the area where the fillet and the main surface data were joined. Visualization makes it obvious.

Contributed by Professor David F. Rogers,
U.S. Naval Academy.

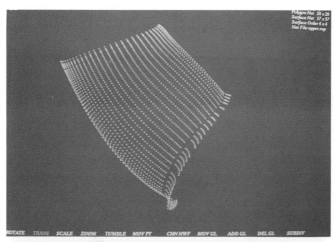

Fig. 2.11
Designer's Data
Visualized with
Rbssd

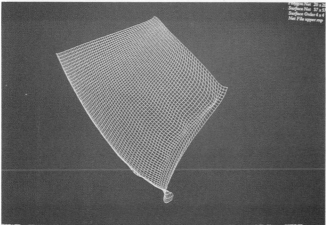

Fig. 2.12
Rational B-spline
Surface

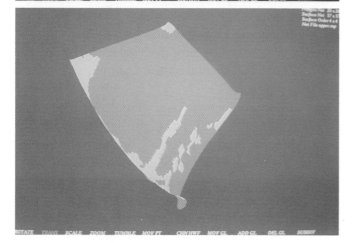

Fig. 2.13
Color Coded
Gaussian
Curvature Surface

Supporting References

Rogers, D. F. and Adlum, L.: Dynamic Rational B-spline Surfaces. Computer Aided Design Journal, invited paper in the commemorative issue honoring Pierre Bezier on his 80th birthday, Computer Aided Design Journal, Vol.22, pp. 609–616, 1990.

Dill, J.C., and Rogers, D.F.: Color Graphics and Ship Hull Surface Curvature. Proceedings of International Conference on Computer Application in the Automation of Shipyard Operation and Ship Design IV (ICCAS '82), 7–10 June 1982, Annapolis, Maryland, pp. 197–205, North-Holland.

2.3.8 Visualization of Forest Growth

Growth of forest

An interactive tree model, FOREST, has been developed at the University of Tokyo to enable the processes of forest formation to be visualized. The model includes a parallel algorithm of individual tree growth which considers both the differences between the species and also the time-dependent interactions among the trees through mutual shading.

Choice of forest to model

A tropical rain forest in the equatorial zone is chosen as a typical case because other types of forest can be derived from it by imposing a set of constraints, such as diminished rain fall and lower tempratures, which slow down the speed of growth processes. The results of the visualization of algorithmically animating a few hundred years of forest growth processes using this model have been validated against the data obtained in experimental observations in Pasoh on the Malaysian peninsula.

Physical properties

The model of individual trees considers the internal properties of trees such as the rate of the light/photosynthesis relationship, the death rate of the branches, and the proportion of the foliage active in photosynthesis.

Figures 2.14 and 2.15 show two frames from a sequence which show the entire life history of the forest. The first shows the initial growth period (1–60 years) and the second shows the higher layer formation processes starting at age 60.

Fig. 2.14
Forest Visualiza-
tion.
Age 60 years

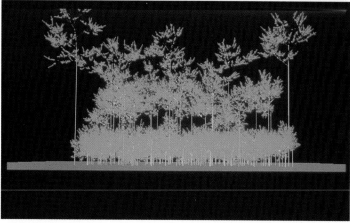

Fig. 2.15
Forest Visualiza-
tion.
Age 250 years

Understanding a typical rain forest and its ecosystem is thus expected to lead to understanding of other types of forests and their ecosystems.

Such models and their visualization can be used to increase our understanding of the growth processes in nature and the way these processes can be affected by apparently minor disturbances in the environment. For example, forestation affects the percentage of carbon dioxide in the atmosphere, which in turn affects global warming, which in turn affects the total area of deserts. Understanding these effects and the relationship between the variables is the key to understanding how to influence the future of the planet. Visualization can play a significant role in furthering this understanding.

*Growth
processes
in nature*

Global modeling

*Information supplied by Professor T.L. Kunii,
University of Tokyo.*

Chapter 3
Explanation of Scientific Visualization Terminology

3.1 Techniques

The schema in Fig. 3.1 outlines some of the current representation techniques.

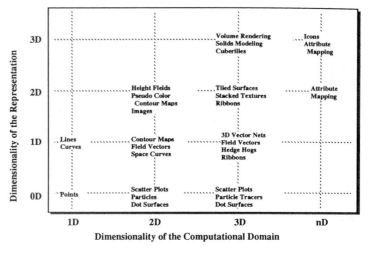

Fig. 3.1
The visualization
Mapping Space:
the mapping from
the computational
domain into the
visualization
domain

The origin of several visualization techniques can be traced back to line-based two-dimensional contour maps. These extensions result in higher-dimensional or more continuous representations as shown in Fig. 3.2.

This chapter outlines techniques that can be used by a scientist confronted with a vast amount of data generated by computer models, remote sensing devices, and automated recording equipment.

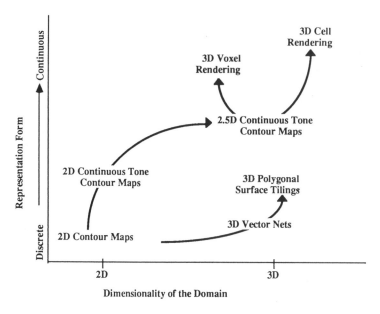

Fig. 3.2
Three-dimensional
extensions of
contouring

On the following pages are some examples of the methods that are chosen to represent quantities in the visualization domain.

Visual Picture

This picture shows a drug molecule reacting with a large enzyme and illustrates the underlying protein structure.

Representation Method

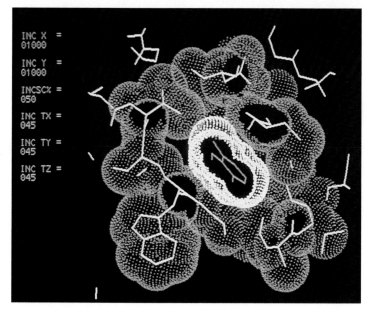

```
INC X =
01000

INC Y =
01000

INCSC% =
050

INC TX =
045

INC TY =
045

INC TZ =
045
```

Fig 3.3
Dot Surface.
Quick method for
small objects.
Time-consuming
and counter-
productive for
larger objects

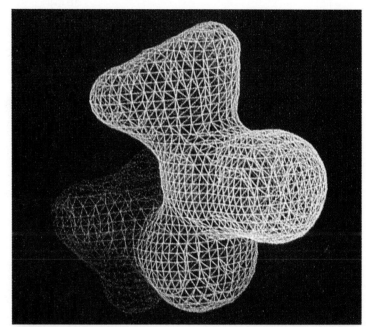

*3D wire frame
representing the
shape of a
surface.*

*Fig. 3.4
Vector Net*

*Fig. 3.5
Polygonal Surface
Surface
represented by
polygons*

Perspective view of a calculated gravity field represented as a 3D smooth shaded polygonal surface, with lighting and shading effects generated from an implementation of the PHIGS PLUS model.

This picture shows part of the North Atlantic where the gulf stream is flowing. The sections show temperature at three different depths with plumes of water demonstrating mixing taking place in the vertical plane.

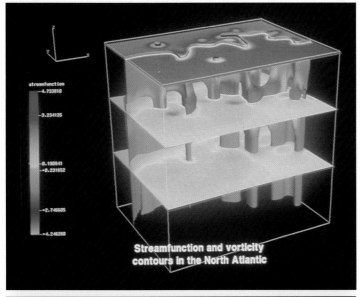

Fig. 3.6
Stacked Contour Map.
Overlaying of 2D cross-sections to represent 3D volumes

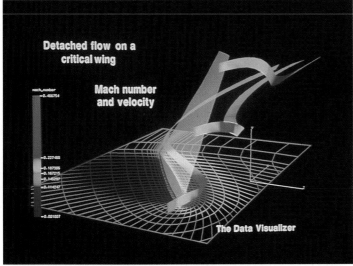

Fig. 3.7
Ribbons and Streamers

This shows airflow round a wing. Color shows one parameter; x, y shows direction; and twisting shows vorticity.

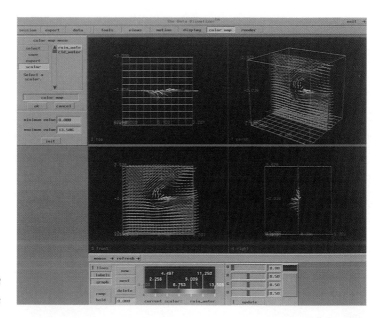

Fig. 3.8
Hedgehogs

A method for showing a direction relative to the surface (hence the term hedgehog spine!). We can of course show a third variable (by the color of the vector).

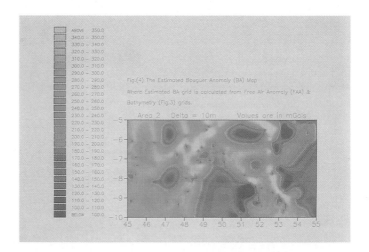

Fig. 3.9
Shaded Contours

This picture shows the use of color to identify areas in the plot between upper and lower threshold values specified by the boundaries of the areas.

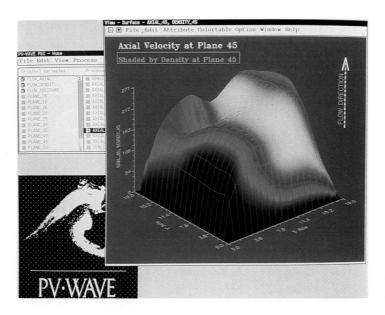

Fig. 3.10

Attribute Mapping

Overlaying an additional data set on an existing 3D one. Height represents axial velocity; shade represents radial velocity. As a turbine pushes fluid through an opening, scientists can observe the density of a particular slice – shown as shading, with red being the most dense.

Representation Method

3.2 Volume Visualization

Volume rendering is used to view 3D data without the usual intermediate step of deriving a geometric representation which is then rendered. The volume representation uses voxels (volume elements) to determine visual properties, such as opacity, color, and shading at each point in the computational domain. Several images are created by slicing the volume perpendicular to the viewing axis at a regular interval and compositing together the contributing images from back to front, thus summing voxel opacities and colors at each pixel. By rapidly changing the color and opacity transfer functions, various structures are interactively revealed in the spatial domain.

Voxels not geometry

Applications   A number of projects in the USA have demonstrated the
benefits to medical and surgical planning from these new
techniques. Further information may be found in Frenkel
(1989), Kaufman (1990), and Upson (1991).

Fig. 3.11
Rendered
Isosurfaces from
Slice Contours a
"nerve cell"

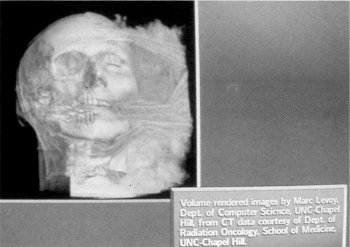

Fig. 3.12
Cell Rendered
Volumetric Image

Figure 3.11 shows paired helical filaments (orange) PHF cracking a cell nucleus (blue). This is used in the study of Altzheimer's disease. The digitized slices are hand contoured; MOVIE·BYU mosaic connects the contours. The "Marching Cubes" algorithm is used for PHF.

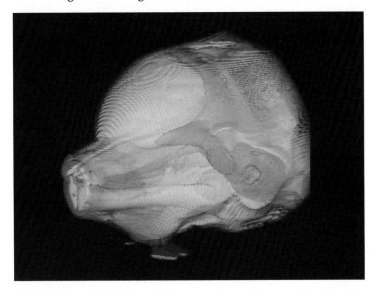

Fig. 3.13
Volume Rendering
of CT Data
"Dolphin Head"
91 slices

3.3 Data Types

3.3.1 Overview of Facilities

As scientific visualization is often concerned with large amounts of data, it is inevitable that methods for organizing it, transferring it, manipulating it, and storing it are of great importance. There are also a wide variety of data formats and utilities for translating between them.

Handling data

Application data is concerned with information at the application level. Data formats are often developed in association with particular application areas. Examples of such formats are Hierarchical Data Format (HDF) developed by the National Center for Supercomputing Applications at the University of Illinois, and Network Common Data Form (netCDF) developed at NSSDC and NASA. Further

Application aspects

information on these formats is contained in Sections 3.3.2 and 3.3.3.

Graphics formats   Graphics data is comprised of information output by the graphics system (e.g., vectors, polygons) which is then converted into appropriate image information. Examples of graphics formats are Computer Graphics Metafile (CGM) and Postscript.

Image data   Image data is the information corresponding to the image on the graphics display screen. For a display with 1000 by 1000 points on the screen we would need 1 million bits to store the information, just for a simple black/white display. With a wide range of colors this amount of information increases, since we need to store a value representing the color for each pixel. There are a number of formats for representing image data, including GPF (Graphical Pixmap Format), TIFF (Tagged Image File Format), Group 3 and Group 4 Fax, VIFF (Visualization Image File Format for the Khoros visualization software), PICT (MacIntosh format), and PCX (IBM format).

Networking implications   In order to be able to transfer image data effectively (particularly over networks) it is important to reduce the size of the image data set to manageable proportions without losing essential information. The Joint Photographic Experts Group (JPEG) and the Moving Picture Experts Group (MPEG) are formulating proposals for standards for single images and multiple frames respectively. JPEG and MPEG are proposals for standards in this area. In addition, fractal compression techniques are being used with considerable success.

Remote sensing   Remote sensed image data contains real information which may be extracted by image processing techniques. This is a well-establised field.

Multi-media   Multi-media systems combine software with facilities for sound, images, graphics, video, and animation to create powerful communication tools. Interest in the area is due to the ability to incorporate data from many sources, and the benefits arising from this. Multi-media products are widely available on personal computers and are moving into the UNIX workstation environment.

In view of the wide variety of data formats currently in use, potential purchasers of scientific visualization systems are advised to check that a given system will handle the data formats required, and also have sufficient capability to handle the volumes of data required.

Choice of system

3.3.2 HDF

The Hierarchical Data Format (HDF) was developed by the National Centre for Supercomputing Application (NCSA) and is available via anonymous ftp.

Hierarchical Data Format (HDF) is a multi-object file format for the transfer of graphical and floating-point data between different hardware platforms. FORTRAN and C calling interfaces for storing and retrieving 8-bit and 24-bit raster images, palettes (color tables), scientific data and accompanying annotations have been developed. HDF allows for the self-definition of data content and aims to be extensible, thereby allowing for the inclusion of future enhancements or compatibility with other standard formats.

File format

Extensible

HDF provides a general purpose file structure that encompasses the following:

Facilities

- makes it possible for the programs to obtain information about the data directly from the file, rather than from another source (e.g. look-up table),
- enables the storage of arbitrary mixtures of data and related information in different files, even when the files are processed by the same application program,
- standardizes the formats and descriptions of many types of commonly used datasets, such as raster images and scientific data,
- encourages the use of a common data format by all machines and programs that produce files containing a specific dataset,
- can be adapted to accommodate virtually any kind of data by defining new tags or a new combination of tags.

HDF currently supports sharing data across machines and systems such as CRAY (UNICOS), Silicon Graphics (UNIX), Alliant (CONCENTRIX), Sun (UNIX), VAX (UNIX), Macintosh (MacOS), and IBM PC (MS-DOS).

3.3.3 NetCDF

National cooperation

The Network Common Data Form (netCDF) was developed as part of Unidata − a U.S. national effort sponsored by the Division of Atmospheric Sciences of NSF. The initiative is managed by the University Corporation for Atmospheric Research. The software is available via anonymous ftp.

Storage and retrieval of data

NetCDF is a data abstraction for the storing and retrieval of scientific data, in particular multi-dimensional data. NetCDF is a distributed, machine-independant software library based upon this data abstraction which allows the creation, access and sharing of data in a form that is self-describing and network-transparent. Both C and FORTRAN interfaces are supported.

Architecture

NetCDF software utilizes the concept of an abstract data type, which means that all operations to access and manipulate data in a netCDF file must be via a defined set of functions provided by the C library interface. As the actual representation of the data is hidden from the application, internal data representations can be changed without affecting the program.

Network transparency

To achieve network transparency, netCDF is implemented on top of a layer of software for external data representation known as XDR. XDR is a nonproprietary standard for describing and encoding data developed by Sun Microsystems, Inc.

Availability

The netCDF software provides common C and FORTRAN interfaces for applications and data. The C interface library is available for many common computing platforms, including UNIX, VMS, MSDOS, and MacOS environments. The FORTRAN interface is available on a smaller set of environments (due to the lack of a standard for calling C from FORTRAN).

XDR has been implemented on a variety of platforms, including SUNs, VAXs, Apple Macintoshes, IBM-PCs, IBM mainframes, and CRAYs.

3.3.4 Databases

The currently accepted storage method for most scientific data is the Relational Database Management System. Many commercial examples are available (e.g., Oracle, Ingres). Data can be extracted using Standard Query Language (SQL) based commands. Some scientific visualization systems have these command interfaces built in (e.g., UNIRAS).

Storage of data

3.4 Current Application Areas

This section provides an overview of application areas where visualization techniques are being used on input data from the real world, processed data, and computer-generated data.

Input data

3.4.1 Cartography

Cartography is rapidly moving from a discipline concerned with the presentation of data (the map) to one concerned with the storage and analysis of spatial data via Geographic Information Systems (GIS). These systems may be used to to store large amounts of information in a database and allow retrieval and display based on user-specified criteria. The visualization is used to select spatial features based on their attributes, or to observe topological relationships with other features. For example, the user may wish to make requests such as the the following:

Analysis of spatial data

- Show me all the regions where forests are adjacent to lakes and which have access by road.
- Show me all the principal roads which have houses within 50 meters.

Interrogating the data

- Display all the houses which have not had their gas service supplies and electricity supplies renewed in the last 30 years.

Data relationships Obviously, there is more information stored in the database than just the terrain. In particular, it illustrates how useful it can be to have other information to do with the same territory available so that it can be interrogated and overlaid on the terrain map.

Project planning The visualization can then be used to plan for work to be done (e.g., by the service industries) in such a way as to minimize costs. Equipment can be moved to an appropriate point in the area and used to supply all the requirements for the work to be done.

3.4.2 Statistics

Visual representation of statistical data is very useful for providing insight and understanding into the data.

3.4.3 Remote Sensing

Satellite and other imaging devices are producing large amounts of data. Many two-dimensional processing methods exist for analyzing this data. New methods are being developed to allow for increasing the dimensionality of the data as the number of frequency bands increases. Visualization methods allow horizontal (two dimensions of space at a given frequency value) and vertical (one dimension of space and one of frequency) sections through the data. An example of the kind of picture produced is shown in Fig. 7.7.

Increasing dimensionality

3.4.4 Archeological Reconstruction

Rebuilding history Data from archeological excavations has been entered into visualization systems to enable partial or major reconstruction to be done, and the resulting constructs to be viewed interactively on a computer display screen. This enables the archeologist to build up a picture of the original buildings, objects, and their relationships.

3.4.5 Molecular Modeling

Chemists and biologists have been using physical models of *Physical models*
molecules for many years to enable the relationships be-
tween the various components to be understood. This is
now more easily and and effectively done by using a com- *Computer models*
puter-based model and interacting with it on a graphics display screen. An example of such a molecule is shown in
Fig. 2.7. Such molecules can be rotated and viewed from var- *Studying the*
ious angles, as well as providing relevant quantitative infor- *molecule*
mation (e.g., potential energies, bond distances, etc.). Analy-
zing X-ray diffraction maps is greatly facilitated by visualiza- *Refining the model*
tion methods. The atomic positions in protein structures
can be adjusted by interaction until they best fit a given electron density map. In the design of new drugs, existing mole- *Design of*
cules can be modified by introducing new molecules into *new drugs*
the overall structure. Such systems often provide a stereo
view capability, where by means of special glasses the user
is able to view the molecule on the screen in full 3D. This
can provide further understanding and insight into the overall structure.

3.4.6 Medical Science

Historically, radiologists have looked at a series of two-di- *From 2D to 3D*
mensional cross-sections and built up mental pictures of
three dimensional structures. However, these are subjective
and can vary from one radiologist to another. In many cases *Accuracy in*
more detailed and accurate three-dimensional information *planning*
can be very useful when planning surgical procedures for *procedures*
complex and/or intricate structures, or in radiation treatment planning. Volume visualization techniques are increas- *Visualizing*
ingly being used to provide three-dimensional information *volumes*
from a series of two-dimensional slices. A case of pelvic reconstruction is outlined in Section 2.3.5, and volume methods are shown in Fig. 3.11–3.13.

3.4.7 Oceanography

Large and complex natural systems

Simulating ocean behavior

Protection of the earth's resources

Modeling the behavior of oceans is increasingly being done using visualization techniques. Often there are a large number of variables involved, such as temperature, salinity, depth, vorticity, etc. Representations are chosen to enable this multi-dimensional data to be viewed on a display screen. Internal structures can be shown and simulations performed. This leads to an increase in overall understanding of ocean behavior. Areas such as these are becoming increasingly important as attention shifts from interplanetary investigations to earth-environment matters such as global warming and the ozone layer. Examples in the area of oceanography are shown in Figs. 3.6 and 7.21.

3.4.8 Computational Fluid Dynamics (CFD)

Air flow over aircraft wings

Fluid flow

Visualization is being used to analyse complex flow systems. Numerical simulations produce values of velocity, temperature, pressure, vorticity, and even tensor fields. A variety of techniques exist for displaying this data. Particle tracers are used in real-time to show aspects of the flow. Interactive CFD is important for tracking and steering solutions. Figures 3.7 and 7.21 show examples.

For further information on application areas, readers are referred to the more detailed reference work *Scientific Visualization – Techniques and Applications* edited by K.W. Brodlie, L.A. Carpenter, R.A. Earnshaw, J.R. Gallop, R.J. Hubbold, A.M. Mumford, C.D. Osland, P. Quarendon, also published by Springer-Verlag, 1992. This volume also has more detailed reference information on data formats.

Chapter 4
Facilities for Scientific Visualization

4.1 Visualization Software Categories

Visualization software has evolved over a period of time and three distinct categories can be identified which appeared in succession. In general the older the category the less the power, memory and storage required to run them. This makes the software in the first category suitable for use in PC or terminal-mainframe environments, and the most recent developments only suitable for the most modern supercomputers or supercomputer workstations. At the same time, because the first and second categories have been around longer, more applications have been developed using them and many products in the market fall into these classes. It is likely in the future that tools using the most modern techniques will appear, but at the present time these techniques are very much in the experimental and developmental stage and will need some time to mature.

Evolution of facilities

4.1.1 Graphics Libraries and Presentation Packages

This is the traditional method for creating ways to view and analyse data.

The libraries interface directly to graphics hardware or provide graphics functionality in software. The user has to supply nearly all the pieces of the application: the main program, the user interface, data handling and geometry mapping. The most basic libraries only supply an interface to the graphics devices (e.g., PLOT10 for Tektronix terminals, HCBS for Calcomp plotters) and some higher-level libraries

Libraries of routines

handle more sophisticated graphic entities such as axes, curve drawing, and so on. Typical examples in common use are the UNIRAS subroutine libraries, DISSPLA, GL (from Silicon Graphics), GKS(2D), PHIGS, DORE (Stardent), and NAG Graphical Supplement.

Pros and cons

The advantage of this type of software is its flexibility and direct control but it suffers from the disadvantage of the large amount of time necessary to write and support code.

PC Graphics

Many PC-based packages such as Harvard Graphics, Slidewrite and CricketGraph have taken on board user-interface functions to provide friendlier software, but still require a great deal of user effort to achieve good results.

4.1.2 Turnkey Visualization Applications

These offer a fixed functionality to solve a limited range of specific problems. The user supplies the data and the computational instructions to the main program and possibly some geometric mapping. The application supplies the main program and rendering and usually has an attractive user interface.

Dedicated to applications

Many products in this category are extremely application-specific and examples in oil exploration, molecular modeling, and architectural modeling are common but of limited use in other fields. They are also very often only available on a very few hardware platforms in common use in these industries – for commercial reasons. More general examples are the UNIRAS interactives, PV-Wave (PVI), Data Visualiser (Wavefront), SunVision (SUN) and VoxelView (Vital Images).

No programming needed!

The user does not have to program these packages and can obtain results very quickly. Their disadvantage is that they have limited extensibility and therefore may often only provide a part of the solution a user requires. They have all reached a high level of maturity and many users applying visualization to their work will probably be using one of these packages.

4.1.3 Application Builders

These offer a series of modules linked by interfaces which are connected interactively at runtime. It combines features from both of the other two categories by providing turnkey solutions for individual parts of the program and the flexibility to customise the final solution adopted. The supplied modules can be replaced by user-written modules as required, providing they conform to the data input/output interface requirements, therefore giving greater extensibility.

In these systems virtually everything the user needs is provided by the program. The user has only to direct the execution path of the program, provide the data, and optionally, their own computational modules if required.

Select the options you need

Applications are constructed by a mouse-driven interface, manipulating icons on screens and linking them with data paths. Once the required modules have been connected and built the program can be executed. New applications can be prototyped very quickly by connecting modules in different ways but the user needs to know how to manage the flow of data through the network, and how to extend the module set.

Constructing applications

Examples are AVS3 (Stardent), Explorer (Silicon Graphics Inc.), apE (Ohio Supercomputer Centre) and Khoros (University of New Mexico). More advanced application builders are currently under development and new advances in visualization techniques and software will extend and improve the application builder functionality. At the present time these products are not mature enough to have had substantial numbers of packages built around them, but these products should be appearing in the future.

Some examples

4.1.4 Choosing a Package

Current work in scientific visualization tends to be done with turnkey application tools – because of their functionality and their ability to process large data sets. However, this does not mean that good visualization work cannot be

What should I use?

done with software libraries and PC packages, but merely reflects the good understanding of these systems that exists in the graphics community. Application builders are still primarily used as research tools, but it is anticipated that more applications will utilize them.

PC graphics survey   PCs are more widely available in the academic/Research Laboratory sphere than any other type of hardware and a thorough review of currently available graphics software has recently been completed by the UK Inter-University Software Committee Working Party and published as a Report.

Data transfer limitations   It is probable that restrictions on internal data transfer bandwidth and graphics display facilities would limit the usefulness of the current PC products as hardware platforms for the majority of applications.

Access via X   For those without workstations, PCs can be utilized as X-servers for such software running on superworkstations, supercomputers, or mainframes, and connected via ethernet or X25 (JANET). Users of PCs therefore can have access to visualization systems remotely and view the results at their desks, albeit at lower graphics resolution and with a time penalty introduced by current network performance.

4.2 Software Costs

4.2.1 Subroutine Libraries and Presentation Packages

You get what you pay for   Costs of subroutine libaries and packages are related to their functionality and degree of sophistication. Those which only provide interfaces to graphics devices (HCBS, PLOT10, HPGL, X11) are bundled with the hardware. Packages with a wide range of higher-level functionality, such as the UNIRAS subroutine libraries, can be fairly expensive. Packages for PC-based operations reflect the prices that PC software can command, and are typically in the range 100–500 pounds sterling. Much of this software is covered by educational deals and is available to the UK community and Research Councils under bulk discount arrangements (e.g., via the UK Combined Higher Educational Software Team – CHEST).

4.2.2 Turnkey Visualization Systems

The cost of these systems reflects the complexity of the systems and the comparative affluence of the targeted application areas! For example, volume rendering products for the petroleum industry are very expensive, but the users can usually afford to pay. At the other extreme, products bundled with, or designed for, particular hardware platforms are very reasonable. Educational deals exist for some of these products.

High-cost areas

4.2.3 Application Builders

At present these systems are either available free (or almost free) in the public domain (e.g., Khoros, apE) or tend to be expensive if they are mainly machine-dependent and bundled in with their hardware platforms (e.g., AVS). In the future, more sophisticated systems may follow this scenario or may become more expensive, if unbundling takes place.

Public domain, or proprietary

4.3 Hardware Considerations (including Hardcopy)

Useful visualization work has been performed on very inexpensive equipment, but there is a growing requirement to perform more complex analysis of increasingly large volumes of data, using more and more sophisticated graphic display techniques. When this is coupled with a demand for much faster response it is obvious that hardware costs for 'ideal' systems could escalate. Although much valuable work has been done on superworkstations attached to a supercomputer (e.g., CRAY) – this is a solution which is not available to many people.

Functionality needed

Costs of
components   The amount of money in a hardware budget will determine what kind of work can be performed, or the speed of
the computation. However, we can identify components
which are important. Systems to perform visualization with
subroutine libraries and packages are fairly modest and ter-
minal connection to a mainframe or a PC-based system cost-
ing less than 2K pounds sterling is likely to be adequate.
Turnkey visualization systems usually require a UNIX
workstation, with color screen and hard disk, which will
cost in excess of 6K pounds. Higher-powered processors,
better quality, faster displays, and substantial hard disk storage will improve throughput but can increase the cost beyond 20K pounds. Application-builder software will only
work properly on high-performance workstations. The ab-
solute minimum configuration will cost around 15K–20K
pounds, but usable systems are likely to exceed 30K. High-
powered systems for complex analysis are likely to cost in
excess of 70K pounds.

Add-on extras   Hidden costs should not be overlooked! These could include items such as high-speed networking access, archive/
backup facilities, sophisticated I/O devices, and – more im-
portantly – hardcopy. A3 color Postscript devices suitable
for use with most workstations, PC's, or on a network, are
available for 10–15K pounds through educational deals. If
it is desired to store graphic images in raster form, then large
amounts of disk space are required.

Costs for training and provision of expert advice and
support also need to be included.

4.4 Vendor Systems Versus Public Domain Systems

Vendor systems   Users are advised to note that vendor systems usually have
software support (e.g., for sorting out software faults and
other difficulties). As part of the licence agreement the user
will usually pay an annual software maintenance fee (typically 5–10% of purchase price). Users also need to enquire

whether such licence agreements entitle the user to receive upgrades and new versions of the software as they become available, if it is desired to continue with the same system for a number of years. Users should note that usually upgrades are included in the original licence agreement, but that major developments or major new versions will often be the subject of separate new licence agreements, for which users have to pay. This is because the vendor has decided it is necessary to recoup research and development costs, and therefore the new version has essentially been made into a new item of software. If the user requires the additional new functions in this software, then he or she is faced with a further licence charge. *New versions may mean further costs*

In this area, as in others, users get what they pay for.

A variety of current vendor systems are detailed in Chapter 7.

Public domain systems often have very limited support, or even none at all. Occasionally the authors and originators indicate they will receive reports of bugs or difficulties, but they cannot necessarily guarantee to provide remedies. Also, future updates and revisions of the system may be more uncertain. However, informal help is sometime available via email discussion lists, where users report their problems and other users with the same software can provide help and assistance. Khoros has such an email discussion list. This list also has the advantage that the Khoros Group at the University of New Mexico are also on the list and so can provide expert technical advice and help as appropriate. However, such help is done on a voluntary basis; there is no contractual commitment. *Public domain systems*

Addressing problems

Public domain systems often offer state of the art facilities, and can be very useful for research and development purposes. They are increasingly subjected to procedures such as those applied to commercial vendor systems, for example, rigorous testing (e.g., Beta testing) before general release to the community, and detailed on-line and hardcopy documentation. They are also essentially free, though occasionally a small distribution fee is charged. Software can *Quality is improving* usually be obtained directly by anonymous FTP across the international communications network. For users with no funds, such software can be very useful indeed.

However, users and potential users should be aware of the following points before committing themselves to using public domain software, especially for large, on-going projects:

Check-list before deciding to use the software

- Software support is usually fairly limited.
- Software support is usually in the hands of a small number of experts (often the designers and originators of the project).
- Future developments (if any) are in the hands of the current developers and the resources available to them.
- The current developers may decide to abandon the current software and work on something completely different, or their managers may move them to work on different projects.
- The software may be sold by the originators or their site to a commercial vendor, who will then only release versions of it as for normal vendor software. The original designers may no longer be involved, and the future directions the product will take become uncertain. An example of this is scenario is apE, which began as a public system and has been recently acquired by a corporation. Further information on this point is given in Chapter 8.

4.5 Summary

Comparing software capabilities

In addition to the obvious functional requirements that users need in the software to meet their specific application, users should also bear in mind the following points when considering how the system is to be used:

- Software support
- Availability of source code
- Range of hardware platforms on which the software is available

- Is a library of graphical subroutines required?
- Can the software be distributed across a number of different platform types (e.g., computational server and workstation)?
- Any graphics interfaces that may be required by higher level software
- X-support
- Data formats supported
- Import formats supported (for reading in information from other sources)
- Export formats supported (for outputting information to other systems)

Thus users of scientific visualization systems need to consider very carefully not just the functions of the system, but also the environment in which is to be run, and the general requirements associated with input of data and export of results to other systems.

List all your requirements

Chapter 5
Outputting Results

5.1 Hardcopy

Neglected topic This topic is included because it is often neglected in the evaluation of scientific visualization systems and because requirements for it only surface when the user has started to use the system and applied it to his or her problem.

Results Users should think carefully about the ultimate destination of their results. Often this includes written papers and reports, and also presentations to funding bodies and conferences.

Hardcopy Intermediate hardcopy is often required for the production of draft reports for circulation within research groups or departments. Thus, although slides and video are usually the preferred medium for the submission for publication, it is often very useful to be able to produce color paper hardcopy for draft purposes.

Color Postscript Color Postscript printers and plotters are now widely available in a variety of paper sizes from A4 to A0. Most visualization software contains drivers for producing color Postscript, since it is a well accepted industry standard.

Stand-alone or networked? For a small research group, a dedicated printer connected to the workstation is a feasible option. For a larger laboratory, or large groups of workstations and users, it is often more economical to consider a larger printer connected via the network. Users then have the capability of generating output of larger size and often greater range of colors. However, it should be noted that large plotters are often expensive to maintain and run (a typical annual maintenance contract can be 7–10% of purchase price).

Areas such as geophysics and seismic applications appli- *Specialized*
cations often use A0-size maps as standard in the industry. *applications*
If these are required then a top of the range color electrostat-
ic plotter will be required.

5.2 Video

Video is becoming an increasingly important medium for   *Color and*
storage and display of real-time simulations for publication   *real-time images*
of research results and presentations at seminars and conferences. It is the only cost-effective medium for the publication of large amounts of color information (1 hour
= 100,000 frames), and which is cheap and easy to copy. It
has a natural interface to the TV technology domain and
provides a portable and easy-to-use medium.

The use of video to demonstrate time-varying and dynamic processes is becoming increasingly important. A sequence of still frames (e.g., on slides) may not convey the
full information relating to the process involved, in a way
that a sequence of moving images can.

The display of real-time simulations offers the user a dynamic analysis tool to supplement other visualization methods.

Video technology is coming within the range of the   *Costs of video*
workstation user by the increasing availability of low-cost
interface boards and also animation software. PCs and
workstations can now be interfaced to a video recorder by
means of a video board, an animation controller, a PAL en-
coder, and a sync generator for around 7 K pounds sterling.
An editing U matic VTR would cost a further 7 K pounds.

The quality of the finished product is proportional to   *Quality of the*
the cost of the system. If broadcast quality is required, then   *result*
the equipment required is currently expensive. However,
much more inexpensive systems (as the above) can produce
reasonable output.

Effective presentation of information via the video medi-   *Viewers can be*
um is a non-trivial task. In particular, almost all viewers of   *stern critics*

such information have become accustomed (unconsciously) to a high level of presentation quality through the programs presented on national and commercial television channels.

Professional advice   Those new to video need to take advice from those with substantial experience in this area, e.g., graphic artists, TV producers, video editors, etc. A close association with those with experience in this area is likely to produce substantial benefits in the quality of the work produced.

5.3 Other Media

CD ROM and laserdisk   Other media include CD ROM and laserdisk. The typical cost of a laserdisk is 700 pounds. This is capable of storing large amounts of picture information, but is expensive unless many copies are required.

Chapter 6
Current Developments and Activities

6.1 USA

Initial impetus for scientific visualization was provided in 1987 by a National Science Foundation (NSF) Panel Report of a Workshop on *"Visualization in Scientific Computing"* (McCormick et al. 1987).

NSF Report

The principal recommendations of the McCormick Report were that national funding should be provided for short and long term provision of tools and environments to support scientific visualization, and to make these available to the scientific and engineering community at large. Such provision was considered to be essential if the enabling tools were to be effectively harnessed by current and future scientists and engineers.

Recommend-ations

Such tools often require access to significant computation resources. A natural focal point for these developments has been the funding of Supercomputer Centers – to provide both the facilities and access to them by the community.

Supercomputer facilities

An example of this at the San Diego Supercomputer visualization Center is the development of network-based general tools purpose visualization tools. These are accessed by 2800 users with 350 different applications. Such users access the facility by a variety of different routes including dial-in lines, national networks, and dedicated high-speed links. In addition to this broad range of provision there are also more specialized tools for high-end applications (e.g., molecular modeling, computational fluid dynamics).

Network-based visualization tools

Specialized applications

Similar provision has also been made at other Supercomputer Centers at Cornell, Pittsburgh, and the University of Illinois at Urbana-Champaign.

Other centers

Workshops   Workshops on scientific visualization have been established by ACM SIGGRAPH and IEEE to address specific as-
pects such as data facilities (to facilitate ease of use and transfer of information), and volume visualization (to enable representation of real 3 D information and to give inside views).
Representatives from the Department of Defense and the Department of Energy have initiated a Working Group to define a Visualization Reference Model. A conference of CG
International was held at MIT, Media Laboratory, in June
1991 with the theme *"Scientific Visualization of Physical Phenomena".* The proceedings have been published as a book by
Springer-Verlag (see Chapter 11 – References).

Visualization   A large number of major universities are establishing vi-
laboratories   sualization laboratories, and often such installations receive
supplementary funding for further proposals in specific application areas. Funding is provided by such bodies as NSF,
DARPA, and NASA. State supercomputers and associated
visualization facilities exist in Ohio, North Carolina, Min-
nesota, Utah, Alaska, and Florida.

Visualization   To provide a forum for the presentation and discussion
conference   of the latest advances in scientific visualization, the IEEE
Technical Committee on Computer Graphics has estab-
lished an international visualization conference, which is
held on an annual basis.

NSF support   In addition, the National Science Foundation is providing funds for the support and promotion of educational initiatives in scientific visualization by means of institutes,
workshops, and summer schools.

Network support   Fast networks are required for distributed and remote visualization. Developments in networking infrastructure are
planned to provide faster communication, interconnection,
and the ability to aggregate computing resources at different
locations on to one particular problem. For example, the
CASA test bed project is funded by the NSF to develop a
1 Gbit/sec network link between Los Alamos National Laboratory, the California Institute of Technology, and San Diego Supercomputer Center, to enable all three resources to be
concentrated on one application simultaneously.

A multi-million-dollar grant has recently been awarded by NSF to California Institute of Technology, Brown University, University of Utah, Cornell University, and the University of North Carolina at Chapel Hill, to explore the foundations of computer graphics and visualization.

Foundation aspects

6.2 UK

A number of centers in UK academic institutions are concerned with application areas such as molecular modeling and computational fluid dynamics (CFD). There are a number of collaborative projects between academia and industry in the areas of parallel processing and scientific visualization. One example, GRASPARC, a Graphical Environment for Supporting Parallel Computing, is a joint project between NAG Ltd., the University of Leeds (School of Computer Studies), and Quintek Ltd. The major objective of the work is to improve the interaction between the computational scientist and the parallel computer through the development of interactive visualization software.

Application areas

VisLab at Sheffield University is engaged in five projects: extending surface reconstruction to irregularly sampled fields; rendering vector and tensor fields; building radiotherapy planning tools; reconstructing cerebral blood vessels from a pair of x-ray projections; and issues surrounding perception.

VisLab

The IBM UK Scientific Centre in Winchester is primarily concerned with scientific visualization and has a Visualization Group, a European Visualization Group, a Medical Imaging Group, and a Parallel Programming and Visualization Group. There are a number of collaborative projects with academia and industry in the areas of parallel processing, user-interface aspects, and medical informatics.

Industry and academia

Natural Environment Research Council (NERC) has a Visualization Advisory Group concerned with evaluating products for the areas of geological surveys and oceanography. Science and Engineering Research Council Engineer-

Research councils

ing Board has evaluated superworkstations in the areas of hardware and software. The present AGOCG Scientific Visualization Workshop which initiated this guide and the Status Report arose out of proposals by the UK Universities funding body for computing (the Computer Board) and the Advisory Group on Computer Graphics (AGOCG).

Video facility   The Rutherford Appleton Laboratory of the SERC, Central Computing Division, has developed a video facility for use by the academic and research community in the UK, and is involved in projects in the areas of oceanography, atmospheric physics, laser design, mechanical engineering, ecological simulation, and CFD.

University of Leeds   The University of Leeds has an interdisciplinary Scientific Visualisation Group and promotes a wide range of software on state of the art hardware platforms to support a variety of applications. (Reference: ACM SIGGRAPH Computer Graphics, June 1992)

Other projects   There are numerous other projects underway in this field – the above is only an indication of the range of work being done.

6.3 Europe

European centers   IBM has a number of European centers actively involved in projects involving Scientific Visualization. These include the European Petroleum Applications Centre (EPAC) in Stavanger, the Paris Scientific Centre which is involved in visualization in the medical area, and the European Scientific Centre in Rome which is involved in engineering and modelling turbulent flow. IBM also has a joint project with the Centre of Competence in Visualization at the University of Aix-Marseilles.

Volume visualization   FhG-AGD in Darmstadt is working on a number of areas, including tools for volume visualization on a variety of platforms, and handling different kinds of data sets.

Workshops   Eurographics arranged a Workshop on Scientific Visualization in April 1990. The proceedings will be available from Springer-Verlag. Further workshops are planned.

Part II

Overview of
Current Systems
and Developments

Chapter 7
Current Vendor Systems in Use

Readers are recommended to read Chapter 4 for a classification and categorisation of scientific visualization systems before reading this chapter. Chapter 4 sets out the overall framework into which the products outlined in Chapters 7 and 8 fit.

Contact addresses are provided for each product at the end of each section.

7.1 Wavefront Technologies, Inc.

Wavefront was founded in 1984 in California and provides graphics products for use on a wide range of UNIX workstations including Silicon Graphics, IBM, Hewlett Packard, DEC and SUN. The company has a well established worldwide sales and support network with its own offices in all the key European countries, including the UK.

Founded in 1984

Wavefront's Visualizer software is designed to help engineers, scientists, designers and graphic artists use the power of today's 3D graphics workstations. There are three products providing professional visual communication to aid rapid understanding.

Visual communication

- The Data Visualizer is designed to speed up the analysis of large volumes of 3D data on any type of grid. It displays many variables at once and uses color and dynamics to create easily understandable images or animation sequences of of complex processes.
- The Personal Visualizer is an easy- to-use image renderer for CAD geometry. It provides photo-realistic images for product designers, engineers and marketing groups.

Summary of Visualization Products

– The Advanced Visualizer includes interactive surface modeling, animation and dynamics, and the ability to render motion sequences and record them on tape or film for presentation. It has interfaces to a wide range of CAD/CAE and dynamics packages and is fully compatible with the other visualizer products.

The Data Visualizer

Data Visualizer

The Data Visualizer is a graphic analysis toolkit for 3 D scalar and vector data on any type of grid – including regular, irregular, and unstructured grids.

Graphical interface

It has a mouse-driven point-and-click interface that allows a wide variety of graphic tools including cutting planes, iso surfaces and iso volumes, particle systems, ribbons, and sheets to be positioned and turned ON and OFF at the click of a button. There is no limit to the number of tools that can be created, grouped, and rendered simultaneously.

Interactive analysis

The Data Visualizer is designed for the interactive analysis of large 3 D volumes where many tools are required for simultaneous analysis, and their rapid combination is a key productivity factor. The user interface therefore provides refined management of tools and screen layout and lends itself well to an environment in which many users require volume throughput.

Animation

The data and all the graphic tools can be animated over time, and there are also common image file formats such as color Postscript for use with DTP printers.

Analysis of fluids and structures

The ability to handle unstructured grids gives the Data Visualizer a strong capability in the next major area of advancement in data visualization. Adaptive unstructured grids allow complex shapes to be defined by the user with relatively simple and intuitive tools. This technology will make numerical analysis of fluids and structures more accessible to the non-expert engineer or designer.

Objects and flows round them

One of the unique features of the Data Visualizer is its ability to use the same analysis tools in the unstructured environment and for multi-block data where individual grids have been created around different components in a flow field. This makes it possible to see a complex assembly such as an entire aircraft, together with the flow conditions around it and its various parts.

Finite Element Analysis applications run exclusively on unstructured grids, and the Data Visualizer provides an assortment of tools for viewing data on the surface of these grids. These include clipping planes and boxes that cut away portions of data volumes and iso-surfaces to view interior detail, while maintaining the exterior view.

Viewing data on unstructured grids

There is also a command language for users who wish to build combinations of tools and results externally – for example from within their solver – and data reader source code is provided to allow on-line network transfer of results from a host directly to the screen of the graphics workstation.

Command language for tool building

Figure 7.1 shows a transparent isosurface of rainwater density in a cloud together with wind velocity flow ribbons that are themselves mapped with a scalar density value. The user interface includes interactive color map editing.

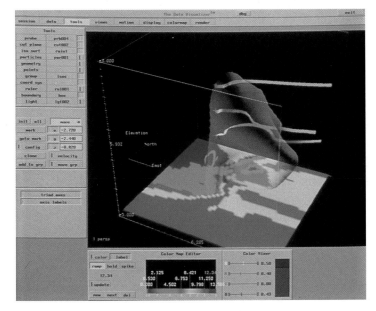

Fig. 7.1

Transparent

Isosurface

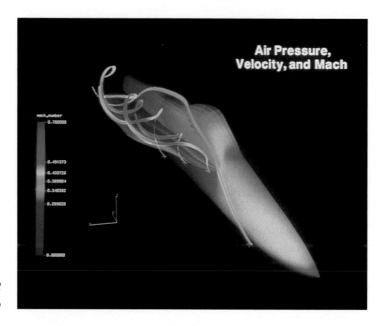

Fig. 7.2
Fighter Fuselage

Figure 7.2 shows computational fluid dynamics analysis of a fighter fuselage. The grid is irregular and contains multiple data blocks and approximately 250 000 nodes. The picture shows air pressure on the fuselage with particle traces mapped with mach number, spiralling around a vortex.

The Personal Visualizer

Personal Visualizer This product was developed for the casual user who needs to postprocess computer-aided design models. It interfaces directly with many leading CAD packages and allows interactive control of lights, cameras, and surface materials to create highly realistic images. The Personal Visualizer provides texture mapping, bump mapping, transparency, refraction and ray tracing, and has a library of over 700 prepared materials as well as its own surface material editor with which new surface textures can be created.

The Advanced Visualizer

This product is for those who wish to create realistic motion sequences, for example an engine assembly in motion, or a spacecraft docking sequence. It provides all the modeling tools needed to create the geometry internally and can also read geometric and stress data from external systems.

Advanced Visualizer

The Advanced Visualizer has sophisticated animation tools and on-line motion channels that can be driven by ASCII data in real time. This latter feature makes it a useful tool in displaying the results of computed dynamic analysis, such as in vehicle crash performance testing. The Advanced Visualizer includes all of Wavefront's state-of-the-art image rendering technology, allowing the user to create virtually any effect that may be required.

Sophisticated animation facilities

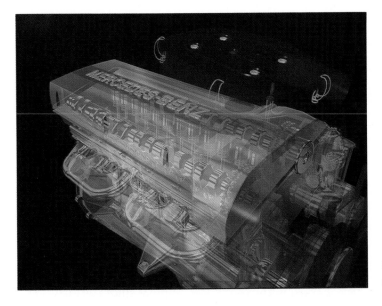

Fig. 7.3
Engine

Figure 7.3 is taken from an animated engine sequence showing all the major parts in synchronised motion seen through the transparent engine block.
Contributed by Peter Stothart, UK Managing Director, Wavefront Technology Ltd.

For further information contact:

U.S.A.   Europe
Wavefront Technologies, Inc.   Wavefront Technologies
530 East Montecito Street   Guldenspoorstraat 21–23
Santa Barbara   B-9000 Gent   Belgium
CA 93103   U.S.A.   Tel: 32-91-254555
Tel: 805-962-8117   Fax: 32-91-234456
Fax: 805-963-0410

United Kingdom
Wavefront Technologies Ltd.
Oakridge House; Wellington Road
High Wycombe
Bucks HP12 3PR   U.K.
Tel: 0494-441273
Fax: 0494-464904

7.2 UNIRAS A. S.

High quality color graphics UNIRAS was established in 1980 with the objective of satisfying the growing need among computer users for a range of high-quality color graphics software. This need arose partly from current requirements to analyse ever increasing volumes of data and partly to utilize fully the high performance graphical output devices coming on to the market.

Raster based UNIRAS software uses raster techniques to deliver a broader spectrum of colors, improved resolution, and greater throughput. UNIRAS therefore makes the most of new hardware technology, while still effectively supporting the traditional vector output devices of an earlier generation.

Pioneering developments Key management and development people at UNIRAS have worked with color raster graphics since the early 1970s and were closely involved in the design of software for the first inkjet plotters. The current UNIRAS product range has evolved from this pioneering work.

Real world application of visualization tools Reflecting the rapid growth of the offshore oil industry at that time, UNIRAS' first commercially available product was a software package to aid exploration companies in their search for oil and gas. This was an early example of the use of scientific visualization tools in real-world applications with considerable strategic benefits. Since then UNIRAS has taken its technology into a number of other application areas, including automotive and aerospace manufacturing, pharmaceutical industry, communications, defense, energy generation and distribution, and environmental management.

UNIRAS software technology comes in two forms. Interactive, user-friendly packages permit non-specialist computer users – scientists, engineers, and managers – to learn to use the extensive facilities quickly and easily; while the range of subroutines provides a choice of powerful tools to help the application programmer integrate high quality graphics with new and existing applications. All UNIRAS products are computer and device independent and comply with accepted international standards.

Interactive modules or library routines

Today UNIRAS is a truly international organization and can list many famous companies, research institutions, and universities among its hundreds of customers. UNIRAS has its headquarters in Denmark, with wholly owned subsidiaries in the USA, UK, France, Germany and Italy, a sales office in Tokyo, and representatives in other parts of the world. Research and development takes place in Denmark and the USA. The major shareholders in UNIRAS are the Danish financial services group Hafnia, the Dutch investment company Halder Holdings, and UNIRAS' own management.

International vendor and clients

UNIGRAPH+2000 is a powerful, fully interactive data visualization system which enables users to:

UNIGRAPH facilities

- retrieve their technical and scientific data from a file or database,
- edit and operate on it in a variety of ways,
- analyse and visualize it quickly and in many forms, from very simple charts to advanced multidimensional surfaces,
- give plots an extra touch of professional presentation quality,
- present the information graphically as hardcopies of the highest quality.

Visualizing datasets

Datasets can be accessed, edited, and analyzed using mathematical, logical, or statistical operators. A comprehensive set of interpolation techniques correctly handles such complexities as regions and barriers, allowing datasets to be visualized as 2D, 3D, or 4D surfaces in color or monochrome.

Wide variety of output devices

The UNIGRAPH+2000 hardcopy system produces high-resolution hardcopies on a wide variety of output devices including raster and vector devices as well as the new generation of Postscript printers. Pictures can also be saved for later use or exported to other systems by the creation of ISO Standard Computer Graphics Metafiles (CGM) or encapsulated Postscript files.

Integrating visualization and presentation

agX/TOOLMASTER is a suite of high-level graphics tools which allows the software developer to easily integrate visualization and presentation techniques into application programs.

Windowing environments

agX/TOOLMASTER programming tools are callable from C and have been developed and optimized for use in an X Window environment. The open systems architecture of agX/TOOLMASTER allows it to be fully integrated with the X Window, OSF/MOTIF and OPEN LOOK windowing environments.

Networked facilities

With agX/TOOLMASTER the application programmer can combine high-level graphics functions with the best features of X such as multiple windows and event handling for interactivity, pixmap generation for animation, and client/server techniques for network computing.

Platforms

agX/TOOLMASTER runs on all major UNIX workstations and supercomputers as well as the VAX/VMS environment, making applications portable across the network. The virtual color system in agX/TOOLMASTER provides X-server independence with its support of monochrome and color displays and various bitplane depths.

Benefits and advantages

The benefits of building an application with agX/TOOLMASTER are:

- The amount of time and code required for building applications in the X environment is greatly reduced,

- Code maintenance and support over the lifetime of an application is also reduced,
- Productivity of programmers is increased by access to high-level single function calls for visualization of numerical data,
- Hardware investments are protected.

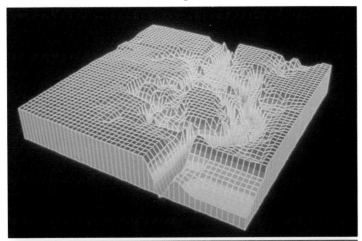

Fig. 7.4
agX/CONTOURS
example

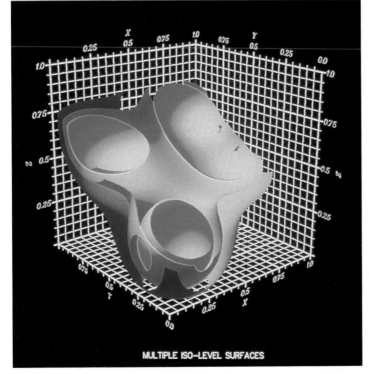

MULTIPLE ISO-LEVEL SURFACES

Fig. 7.5
agX/VOLUMES
example

Commitment to standards

UNIRAS technology is based on standards, and in the future UNIRAS will continue to develop products that offer flexibility together with computer and device independence. The further development and enhancement of both the UNIRAS interactive packages and subroutine libraries will continue to provide high-quality graphics solutions to both end users and application programmers.

Ongoing developments

Research and development now takes place in both Europe and the USA in order to reinforce the global scope of the company's products. Future developments will also take place with the cooperation of both UNIRAS users and the computer hardware vendors. The UNIRAS network of local subsidiaries in Europe, USA, and Japan will enable the company to continuously strengthen local sales and support activities.

Contributed by Mike Bundred,
General Manager UNIRAS Ltd.

For further information contact:

Denmark
UNIRAS A.S.
376 Gladsaxevej
DK-2860 Soborg
Denmark
Tel: 45-31-672288
Fax: 45-31-676045

Germany
UNIRAS GmbH
Niederkasseler Lohweg 8
W-4000 Dusseldorf 11
Federal Republic of Germany
Tel: 0211-5961017
Fax: 0211-5961019

United Kingdom
UNIRAS Ltd.
Ambassador House
181 Farnham Road
Slough SL1 4XP
U.K.
Tel: 0753-579293
Fax: 0753-821231

7.3 Precision Visuals, Inc.

Engineers, scientists and researchers have a common need   *Visual data*
for visual data analysis (VDA) in order to understand and   *analysis*
use their data. A common requirement is for large datasets
and fast graphics with analytical capabilities such as mathe-
matics, statistics, signal processing, and image processing.

Precision Visuals Workstation Analysis and Visualiza-   *Visualization*
tion Environment (PV-WAVE) is a powerful software system   *environment*
which lets users display, reduce, analyse and re-display large
multi-dimensional data sets.

As an example, Figure 7.6 exhibits temperature, carbon
monoxide, and sulfur dioxide contents in a city's air for one
year. The 3D surface allows observation of how all the parameters interact, and integrates the three variables in one
plot. Thus relationships between parameters can be visualized. Menus also allow highlighting and magnification of a
specific dataset.

Visual Data Analysis and PV-WAVE improves upon tra-   *User interaction*
ditional data analysis by allowing the user to control data

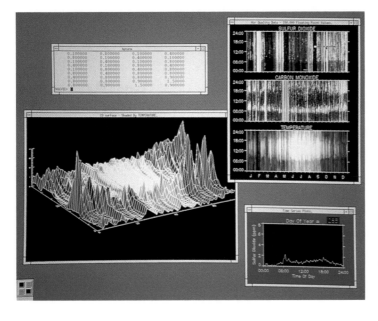

Fig. 7.6
Test Engineering
– Air Quality Data

analysis by user interaction with visual representations. The features of PV-WAVE are:

- Reads and defines large, multi-dimensional datasets
- Tools for fast manipulation and subsetting
- Quick graphical displays of immediate results
- Immediate user interaction
- Advanced graphic tools for animating and displaying multidimensional data

Increase in productivity   VDA techniques are invaluable for scientific discovery and engineering analysis. They offer impressive advantages, including increases in productivity and a means for visual communication with colleagues.

PV-WAVE   PV-WAVE is interactive software for visualizing and analyzing technical data. It consists of a set of high-level, interpretive commands and procedures that provide:

Features
- Data access, reduction and analysis
- 2D and 3D graphics
- Dynamic graphics
- Image processing and manipulation
- Application development

Application areas   PV-WAVE is being successfully applied in the following application areas:

Laboratory Science
- to visualize and analyze data from analytical instruments
- to develop instrument automation systems
- to create custom laboratory information systems

Test Engineering
- to visualize vibration, heat transfer, and emissions test data
- to compare prototype performance with theoretical expectations
- to implement quality control systems in manufacturing environments

Real-time Data Acquisition and Control
- to build automated remote sensing systems
- to manage water quality and sewage systems
- to monitor atmospheric conditions
- to create simulations based on real data

Space Exploration and Astrophysics
- to reconstruct planetary and stellar environments
- to study geodynamics in planets and satellites
- to study seismology
- to simulate astronomical events and objects

Computational Fluid Dynamics
- to identify flow patterns such as shock waves, vortices, and shear layers
- to apply CFD research to aeronautics, automotive design, weather forecasting, and oceanography
- to analyze data from thermal dynamics, fluid dynamics and nuclear reactions

Finite element modeling and analysis
- to assure quality and reliability in computations involving field equations
- to apply finite element pre- and postprocessing methods to such areas as aircraft design and stress analysis in building components

Imaging – medical and remote sensing
- to postprocess remote sensing data
- to display and analyse bioscience imagery, including NMR/MRI, X-Ray, CAT, and electron microscopy

Earth Resources
- to interpret seismic data
- to analyze well logs for locating mineral deposits
- to make meteorological predictions
- to compile and combine raw data for mapping

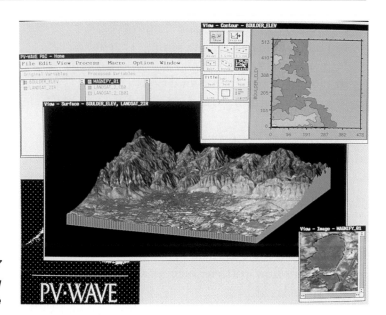

Fig. 7.7
Remote Sensing
– Landsat Image

In Figure 7.7. PV-WAVE Point and Click subsets this satellite image in multiple windows using the toolbox. The picture shows the Boulder Valley east of the Rocky Mountains. The Boulder Reservoir is highlighted in the smaller windows.

Other products   Other members of the PV-WAVE family of visual data analysis software products include:

Numerical analysis   PV-WAVE : NAG – features the powerful numerical analysis capabilities of the NAG Workstation Library with the sophisticated visualization and data analysis functions of PV-WAVE to create a single tightly integrated system, allowing access to 172 subroutines and functions from the NAG library through a seamless link.

Programming   PV-WAVE Point and Click – combines the power and
not needed   functionality of PV-WAVE with an easy to use Point and Click mouse-driven interface that allows technical professionals to access, analyse, and visualize their data, without the need to program.

For further information contact:

U.S.A
Precision Visuals, Inc.
Lookout Road
Boulder
CO 80301
U.S.A.
Tel: 303-530-9000
Fax: 303-530-9329

United Kingdom
Precision Visuals International, Inc.
Royal House
1–4 Vine Street
Uxbridge
Middlesex UB8 1XF
U.K.
Tel: 0895-235131
Fax: 0895-272299

Germany
Precision Visuals
International GmbH
Lyoner Stern
Hahnstrasse 70
W6000 Frankfurt/Main 71
Federal Republic of Germany
Tel: 49-69-6690150
Fax: 49-69-6666738

7.4 Stardent Computer, Inc.

AVS is an advanced interactive visualization environment for scientists, engineers, and technical professionals. AVS supports geometric, image and volume datasets – the user can interactively select the appropriate menu option. No programming is required.

Interactive visualization

For the more sophisticated user, the AVS Network Editor can be used to build processing networks into which user-developed modules and computational programs can be integrated easily.

Visual Network Editor

Modules can by dynamically added, connected, and deleted. Modules are only re-executed when new data is required or an input parameter is changed. Modules have control panels for interactive control of input parameters by on-

Modular approach

screen sliders, file browsers, dials and buttons. The control panel is automatically generated when a module is connected into the network.

Building applications

The complete network can be saved with all the user defined interactive controls and layout specifications as a complete application. This can then be invoked directly, bypassing the standard AVS menus and the Network Editor.

Integration of user programs

User programs can be coupled into the network to allow real-time visualization of dynamic simulations. This allows the user to transform existing batch programs into interactive visual applications.

Further modules

AVS has a wide range of data input, filter, mapper and renderer modules. User-written programs or subroutines in FORTRAN or C can be easily converted into AVS modules.

Filters

Filters transform data into data or geometry into geometry. Some filters convert the output data of widely-used applications into displayable form. AVS includes filters for applications in engineering analysis, computational fluid dynamics (CFD), chemistry and other fields. Other filters process commonly used data formats such as the Brookhaven Protein Databank (PDB) molecular structure format, or graphics formats such as MOVIE.BYU and Wavefront Technologies.

New filters

New filters can be developed by means of templates and geometric conversion utilities.

Mapping

Mappers transform data into geometry. Multiple visualization techniques can be selected to suit the problem being studied. Examples of mappers include: isosurfaces of a 3D field; 2D slices of a 3D data volume; 3D meshes from 2D elevation datasets.

Renderers

Renderers display geometry, images, and volumes on screen. AVS networks can incorporate multiple rendering modules, including a fully-featured 3D geometry renderer, an image display renderer, and a range of volume renderers. Graphic images may also be output to hardcopy devices or video tape.

Image processing

AVS provides a complete image display capability, including real-time pan and zoom, rotation and transformation, flipbook animation, and support for 8-bit, 24-bit, and floating point images. Imaging filters include look-up table operations such as contrast stretching, pseudo-coloring, and histogram balancing, as well as data resizing operations such as interpolation.

AVS takes image processing a step further by generalizing these modules for 3D volume imaging. AVS provides a variety of tools for rendering volume data; a real-time isosurface generator; a unique transparent volume renderer which creates real-time, semi-transparent images with full rotational and lighting control; generation of geometric objects such as arbitrary slicing surfaces, dot surfaces and vector nets; and VBUFFER, a unique, high-quality volume renderer.

Volume imaging

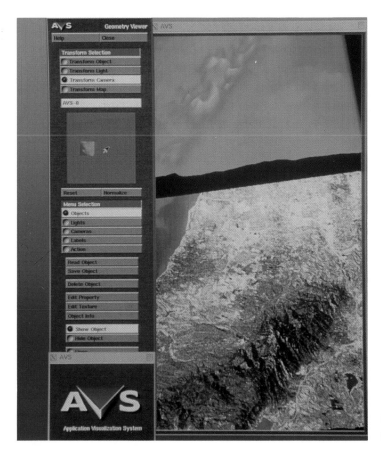

Fig. 7.8
Stardent AVS

Geometry viewing

The AVS Geometry Viewer gives full control with simple menu-driven parameter selections. It offers wireframe, Gouraud, or Phong shading; 16 individually controlled colored light sources, selectable as point, directional or spot lights; surface properties such as specularity and transparency; real-time texture mapping and anti-aliasing.

Different views

AVS allows creation of multiple windows with different views of the same geometric object or simultaneous display of multiple objects.

Hierarchies

Scenes with hierarchies of objects can be created and manipulated individually or as one or more groups. Scenes can be saved, with all viewing selections preserved for later redisplay. Sequences of images can be created and saved, and

Animated views

the sequence cycled through to provide animated views of dynamic behavior in real time.

Platforms

AVS is designed for portability and multi-platform support, from desktop systems to supercomputers. Written in C, AVS runs in a UNIX X-Window environment. The geometry renderer is designed to support a variety of graphics display subsystems including the standards PHIGS and PHIGS+, Stardent's advanced rendering and display environment, DORE (Dynamic Object Rendering Environment), and other display list or immediate mode graphics interfaces.

AVS modules are a convenient means of exchanging new computational and visualization software.

AVS is supplied free with every Stardent visualization system. Licensing of the software is available for other platforms.

Figure 7.8 shows 3D terrain elevation mapping using Stardent's AVS package. The area shown is Orange County, southern California.

Figure 7.9 shows the visualization of electron orbital within a hydrogen atom using Stardent's AVS package.

From information supplied by Stardent Computer Ltd.

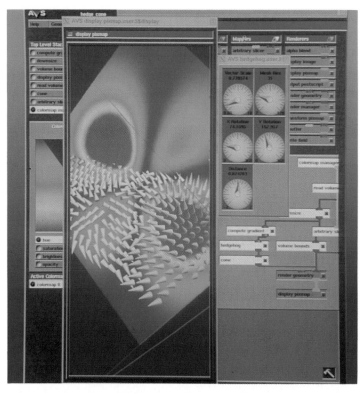

Fig. 7.9
Visualization of
Electron Orbit

For further information contact:

USA
Stardent Computer, Inc.
6 New England
Tech Center
521 Virginia Road
Concord MA 01742
U.S.A.
Tel: 508-287-0100
Fax: 508-371-7414

International Headquarters
Stardent Computer
Hagenauer Strasse 42
W-6200 Wiesbaden 1
Federal Republic of Germany
Tel: 49-611-22037
Fax: 49-611-260181

United Kingdom
Stardent Computer Ltd.
7 Huxley Road
The Surrey Research Park
Guildford Surrey GU2 5RE
U.K.
Tel: 0483-505388
Fax: 0438-505352

7.5 Silicon Graphics, Inc.

Visual processing Silicon Graphics is the world's leading manufacturer of visual processing systems. Visual processing allows staff and researchers to work with data in a more natural, intuitive way – graphically. In addition, Silicon Graphics designs, manufactures and markets computational systems used by engineers, scientists and animation professionals for design and analysis of 3D objects and for general purpose technical computing. By employing RISC technology and proprietary VLSI components to provide both high-performance computing and high-performance graphics, Silicon Graphics continues to deliver amongst the most powerful systems available for engineering and scientific applications.

Four levels As part of its visual processing software, Silicon Graphics
of products is offering four modular software products which fit into different levels between application and source code. Figure 7.10 shows how these products relate to each other. Moving up the chart shown in Fig. 7.10 away from the source code and toward the application makes it easier for the user to use a product without specialist knowledge, but this loses some of the flexibility at the source level.

Upper and Often this difference between the upper and lower levels
lower levels is partly or wholly obscured by the proliferation of tools and facilities currently available in the market place.

Graphics The products depicted in Fig. 7.10 are as follows: GL is
Library GL the Graphics Library that has been available from Silicon Graphics for a number of years, and is now gaining acceptance with other hardware suppliers. This provides the basic system calls required to address the 3D graphics hardware incorporated into every Silicon Graphics system. It is a set of calls that can be included into source code, which may be written in a programming language. Above this level is a graphics toolkit which provides a library of standalone GL calls that have been developed to address a wide range of graphics problems and which is available to be incorporated into software developers' products.

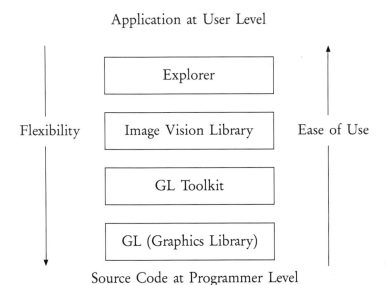

Fig. 7.10
Levels of products

The more significant products are at the highest level. **Higher level products**
Image Vision Library (IL) is an object-oriented, extensible toolkit for creating, processing and displaying images on all Silicon Image Graphics workstations. The IL toolkit provides image-processing application developers with a robust framework for managing and manipulating images. The toolkit is specifically designed to provide a constant software interface to hardware that may change underneath, thus ensuring that applications can continue to run unchanged in the future. **Image Vision Library**

The Image Vision Library consists of a shared library developed in C++, with interfaces for C and FORTRAN. It has a core set of more than 70 image processing operators, and is user-extensible for specific needs. Silicon Graphics provides a set of data abstractions and access functions to make it easy to augment the IL toolkit's image operators and design new ones. **Image processing operators**

Image data sets have a wide variety of formats. The IL toolkit allows new file formats to be integrated into the library. The toolkit currently supports three standard formats: SGI, and extended version of TIFF, and a simple tiled format called FIT. **Image data set formats**

Image manipulation   The IL toolkit provides an efficient model for the manipulation of image data and image attributes. The toolkit's image model includes a configurable cache to allow access to, and processing of, the very large images common in many disciplines. IL provides a common interface for image manipulations, while requiring little or no programmer knowledge of the image's internal structure of format. IL imple-

Data processed on demand   ments a demand driven execution model, such that data is processed only on demand. This model is based on the same cached-image model as file images. This technique enables an application to process just the area of interest, providing significant benefits in terms of reduced I/O and improved system performance.

Visualization facilities   The fourth product is called Explorer. This is a true applications developer package. It provides visualization and analysis functionality for users whose needs are not met by commercial software packages, or who want to extend existing systems with their own algorithms and techniques.

Customised application building   The software environment falls into the category of Application Builders – environments that consist of functional program pieces called modules which are visually connected together through a point-and-click user interface into a data flow style network. This flexible and interactive environment of building application programs by choosing from a suite of functional modules is the true power of the system.

Modular approach   Modules are the building blocks of the visualization software and cover a wide range of functionality. Because the software environment encompasses a distributed execution model, modules may execute on the local workstation or on other platforms on the network. Users can easily integrate their existing algorithms into the system in the form of new modules. Through point-and-click selections, a model-building facility is provided which generates the code needed to make the user's algorithm into a visualization software module. Modules generally fall into the following categories:

- Input
  Modules that read data files
- Feature Extraction and Analysis
  Modules that produce data from data (e.g., extract a planar slice from a volumetric dataset)
- Geometric Representation
  Modules that produce geometry-based display lists from data
- Renderers
  Modules that produce images from geometry, volumes or images
- Output
  Modules that write to disk

System Data Types are the data formats for passing data through the system. The system data types are powerful and abstracted, and each can represent an entire class of data as well as a very specific instantiation of the data. Date types are as follows: *Data types*

- Parameter
  This data type conveys widget interaction to the module. Parameters are scalar quantities including long integer, double precision, floating point, and character string.
- Lattice
  This is the most widely used data type. It is essentially a multi-dimensional array with two major components: data stored at nodes of the lattice, and a coordinate mapping.
- Pyramid
  This data type combines lattices with connectivity in a hierarchical structure. The depth of this structure is arbitrary.
- Geometry
  This data type contains a hierarchical geometrical scene description. The geometric description contains all information concerning geometric objects and their attributes, cameras, lights, etc.

- Unknown
  The unknown type is an uninterpreted array of bytes.
  The organisation and interpretation is left to the pro-
  grammer.

Widening the use   IRIS Explorer is a key part of Silicon Graphics' new techni-
of visualization   cal computation environment, aimed at making the company's industry-leading visualization technology more accessible to the broad range of workstation users. With IRIS Explorer, users view data and create applications by visually
connecting software modules into flow chart configurations
called module maps. Modules, the building blocks of IRIS
Explorer, perform specific program functions such as data
reading, data analysis, image processing, geometric and volume rendering, and many other tasks. Modules can be executed across heterogeneous platforms, delivering powerful,
resource-efficient distributed computing capabilities to application users and developers.

The following pictures were created by Silicon Graphics
using AVIRIS data, courtesy of the Jet Propulsion Laboratory. AVIRIS data is made up of 224 spectral bands. The images were created by traversing through the data in the spectral
dimension, and show spectral responses and histograms of
the data.

Figure 7.11 is a general view of the user-interface showing an image of San Francisco with several multi-spectral analyses being carried out. (Created by Silicon Graphics using
AVIRIS data, courtesy of the Jet Propulsion Laboratory.)

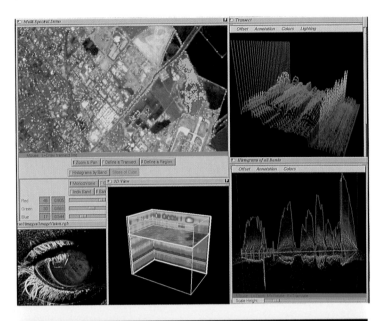

Fig. 7.11
Multi-spectral
Analyses

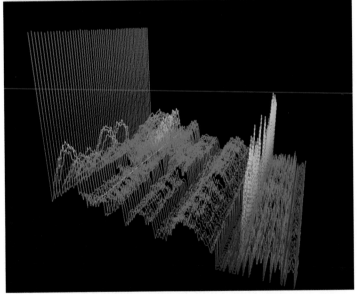

Fig. 7.12
Spectral
Signatures

Figure 7.12 contains an isometric view showing spectral signatures for a number of pixels along a specific transect of the original image. Vertical scale is the radiance, horizontal scales are position and wavelength.

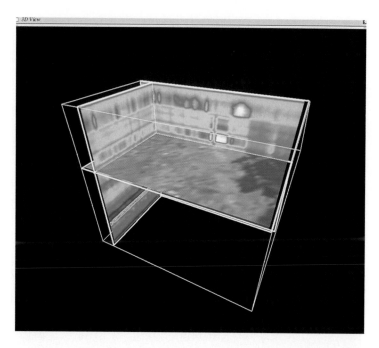

Fig. 7.13
Chair Diagram

Figure 7.13 is a chair diagram of multi-spectral image data. The horizontal plane shows an image at a particular wavelength. The vertical planes are slices at a given X,Y location showing radiance at the spectral wavelengths which have been recorded.

From information supplied by Mark Goossens, Education and Research, Silicon Graphics Ltd.

For further information contact:

USA	Europe	United Kingdom
Silicon Graphics, Inc.	Silicon Graphics	Silicon Graphics Ltd.
2011 N. Shoreline Boulevard	International	Forum 1 Station Road
P.O. Box 7311	18 Avenue Louis Casai	Theale Reading
Mountain View	CH-1209 Geneva	Berks RG7 4RA
CA 94039-7311	Switzerland	U.K.
U.S.A.	Tel: 41-22-7987525	Tel: 0734-306222
Tel: 415-960-1980	Fax: 41-22-7988230	Fax: 0734-302550
Fax: 415-961-0595		

7.6 Sun Microsystems, Inc.

7.6.1 SunVision –
Sun's Visualization Software Package

SunVision is a software platform with which application developers and sophisticated end users can develop visualization applications. It includes two programming interfaces (for image processing and high-quality rendering), and Open Windows-based tools for image processing, volume rendering, manipulation of 3D geometric data, high-quality rendering and movie loop display. The tools and libraries are highly integrated so that data and images can be shared among them.

Visualization applications

SunVision 1.1 runs on any 8-bit color SPARCstation/Sun-4 Workstation and on Sun workstations equipped with the true color VX/MVX visualization accelerators. No special purpose hardware is required. If a VX or VX+MVX visualization accelerator is present in the system, the SunVision applications are transparently accelerated.

No special purpose hardware add-ons required

7.6.2 SunVision Programming Interfaces

SunVision provides two libraries for visualization tasks (image processing and high-quality rendering), and one utility library. Future releases will include an additional library interface for volume rendering. In addition, SunVision is designed to work in an integrated fashion with XGL, Sun's 3D interactive graphics library.

Libraries

SunIPLib is Sun's image processing library, providing extensive image processing functionality. It consists of C-callable functions for:

Image processing

- arithmetic and logical operations
- spatial filtering
- Fourier domain processing
- image analysis
- geometric operations

In addition, there are library functions to create and manipulate subimages and regions of interest.

Images can have multiple bands, and can have unsigned byte, signed 16-bit short, or 32-bit floating point data types. Additional imaging functions can be added to the library.

High-quality For high-quality rendering, SunVision provides a Ren-
pictures derMan function library and a RIB (Renderman Interface Bytestream) protocol interpreter. The RenderMan interface provides a way to describe geometry, scenes, the camera, and lights so that computer images can be generated from this information.

RenderMan Users of the RenderMan interface specify a set of procedures that describe a scene. Object color and location, lighting, and viewer perspective can all be specified. The RenderMan shading language provides a way to create shaders specific to a given scene.

The SunVision RenderMan function library is compliant with version 3.1 of the RenderMan Interface Specification. It also supports the following optional features:

- solid modeling
- programmable shading
- displacements
- texture mapping
- environmental mapping (partial implementation)
- bump mapping
- volume shading (partial implementation)

The following surface shader options are also provided:

- general (the default)
- the 6 standard RenderMan surface shaders (plastic, painted plastic, metal, shiny metal, matte, and constant)
- the 2 standard RenderMan atmosphere shaders (depth cue and fog)

7.6.3 SunVision Window-based Tools

Visualization tools SunVision also provides Open Windows-based visualization tools for image processing (SunIP), volume rendering (SunVoxel), 3D graphics manipulation (SunGV), high quality rendering (SunART), and movie loop display (SunMovie). Additionally, there is an interactive colormap editor that is accessible by each tool. These tools can be used "as is" by sophisticated end users, or as "application prototypes" which developers can tailor to a specific application.

Each window-based tool is an independent program that communicates with a shared parameter database program (PMGR), which, in turn, communicates with a user interface management program (SunVIF). The user interface for each tool can be changed at run time, with no programming. Additional programs can be easily added to the SunVision user interface.

Shared information

SunIP and SunART are tools that implement the image processing and RenderMan functions described above. The source code for SunIP and SunART is provided in the form of examples for using these libraries, along with SunVIF and PMGR.

SunVoxel is an interactive tool for the generation of images from volume data. It consists of window-based rendering and analysis functions. With SunVoxel, volume data can be manipulated and viewed in two modes:

Images from volume data

(1) manipulate the entire volume, using orthogonal or oblique slicing planes where needed, and view internal structures using ray-casting, and
(2) extract and view 2D slices of the volume data in a "light box" mode. There is also a "cloud" mode for displaying data stored in point cloud format.

SunVoxel supports unsigned byte data on uniform rectangular grids. Data filters are provided to convert TAAC-1 volume data to the SunVision data format.

SunGV is used to interactively view 3D geometric data. It can also be used to edit scenes that can be input to SunART for final rendering. SunGV provides wireframe and Gouraud shaded display of polygon and patch data types. Scenes can be composed of a series of objects which are organized hierarchically in a tree structure. Editing functions allow the user to select, copy, paste, cut, and delete objects

Viewing 3D geometric data interactively

in the hierarchy. Objects can be transformed and assigned attributes, such as color, opacity, specularity, texture, etc. Functions are also provided for changing the viewing and projection parameters, and for defining the lighting model, which supports up to 32 light sources. The source code for SunGV is provided as an example for using the XGL graphics library along with SunVIF and PMGR.

Movies   SunMovie is a tool for the display of image and movie loop data. Images and sequences of images generated by other components of SunVision can be viewed using this tool.

7.6.4 The VX and MVX –
Sun's Visualization Accelerators

Accelerators Sun's new visualization workstations are powered by the new VX and MVX accelerator boards. The VX accelerator is a successor to the TAAC-1, incorporating added features, including twice the memory, double the performance, multiple windows, and a lower price.

The MVX is a multi-processor accelerator that can be added to a VX system, providing performance of more than 4–6 times the TAAC-1. Both accelerate SunVision's visualization tools and libraries, and XGL, Sun's graphics library.

Application areas VX and MVX systems are for developers who require a combination of imaging and graphics to develop visualization software. Target markets include medical imaging, remote sensing, earth resources, scientific visualization, and AEC.

7.6.4.1 Features and Benefits
VX

Characteristics ● Accelerates SunVision and XGL.
● High-performance Intel i860 processor (40 MIPS, 80 MFLOPS) for high-speed integer and floating point computation required by visualization applications.
● Dual frame buffer architecture with 32-bit VX and 8-bit GX accelerated frame buffers on one board; a digital keying technique is used to cleanly integrate the VX windows into the system display.

- Transparent integration of multiple VX windows into the GX Open Windows environment; four independent colormaps are available for use by the multiple VX windows, with a fifth colormap allocated for the GX.
- Reconfigurable VX frame buffer can be used to display 24-bit true color plus 8-bit alpha, or four independent 8-bit channels.
- Supports Sun's new 1280x1024 @ 67 Hz format as well as the existing 1152×900 @ 66 Hz format.
- Single 9U VME board.

MVX
- Provides additional acceleration of SunVision and XGL.
- Four Intel i860 processors, offering a total of 160 MIPs and 320 peak single-precision MFLOPS (240 peak double-precision MFLOPS).
- Four Mbytes of memory per processor for fast data and image access.
- High-speed data bus for fast, smooth data and image transfer between the MVX and VX.
- High-speed control bus for transfer of commands between the MVX and VX, eliminating VME overhead.

Software Included
- SunVision and XGL for the most integrated, easy-to-use visualization environment, with the widest range of graphics and imaging functionality, in the industry.
- Complete set of C-development tools, including compiler and debuggers, for application developers.

For further information, contact:

Doug Schiff
SunVision Product Manager
P.O. Box 13447
Research Triangle Park
NC 27709
U.S.A.
Tel: 919−469−8300
Email: doug.schiff@East.Sun.COM

Sun's new VX visualization accelerator delivers high-performance across the full range of visualization techniques, including image processing, volume rendering, 3D graphics, and high-quality rendering. A multiprocessor MVX board can be added to the VX model to boost performance to 160 MIPS and 320 peak single precision MFLOPS. The VX and MVX accelerate Sun's XGL and SunVision software libraries. Shown here are a Gouraud shaded teapot, a volume-rendered air duct, and a 2D Landsat image, running in Sun's Open Windows environment. (Figure 7.14)

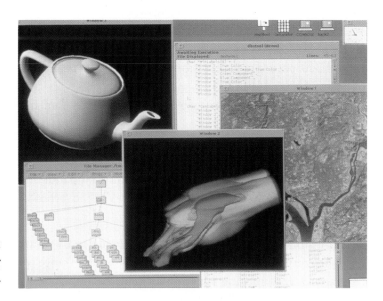

Fig. 7.14
VX and MVX
Overview

SunVision is a software toolkit for integrated, desktop visualization on any SPARC-based Sun Workstation with a GX or VX accelerated color frame buffer. It delivers image processing, volume rendering, interactive 3D graphics viewing, and high-quality rendering in Sun's Open Windows environment. Figure 7.15 shows a wireframe model of a tea set, a volume rendered CT head, SunVision's colormap editing tool, filtered images, and a photorealistic rendering of geometric objects.

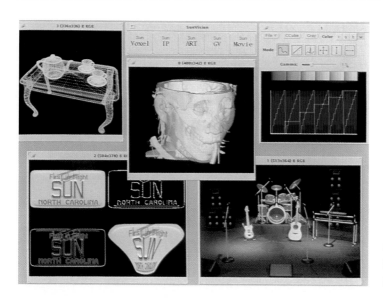

Fig. 7.15
SunVision
Overview

A new volume rendering technique called "splat", developed by Lee Westover while at the University of North Carolina, was used to render different views of a 256×256×96
CT scan of a human head (Figure 7.16). The four images depict the skin and bone surfaces. The transparency of the
skin is changed in each picture. The upper left view shows
an intermediate step as the data is being rendered from back
to front. The algorithm is easy to parallelize; these images
were generated on a Sun VX+MVX visualization accelerator, with four processors doing the data shading and one
processor compositing the samples into the final image.

SunVision's volume rendering tool, SunVoxel, generates
images from 3D volumetric data. The data can be manipulated and viewed in one of several modes, including slice
mode, ray-casting, surface editing mode, point cloud mode,
and light table mode. In Figure 7.17, a 256×256×96 CT scan
of a head is rendered in ray-casting mode with semi-transparent substances. The user can easily assign color and opacity properties to ranges of data values that represent areas of
interest.

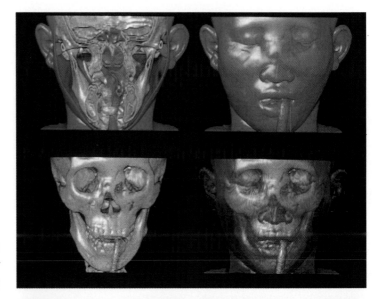

Fig. 7.16
Four Views of CT
Head

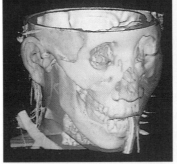

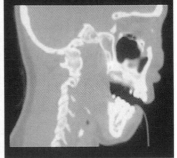

Fig. 7.17
Semi-transparent
CT Head

Fig. 7.18
2D slice from
CT Head

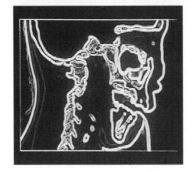

Fig. 7.19
Filtered 2D slice
from CT Head

SunVision's volume rendering tool, SunVoxel, lets the user extract 2D slices from the 3D volume. In Figure 7.18 a single slice from the 256×256×96 CT scan of a head (shown in Fig. 7.17) is selected and displayed. The image can be scaled to any size, and regions can be marked and deleted. The image can be saved to a file for future use.

Sun's image processing library, SunIPLib, provides software for analysis and manipulation of images. SunIPLib provides arithmetic operations, logical operations, spatial filtering, Fourier domain processing, morphological operations, geometric operations, statistics, and more. The image saved in Fig. 7.18 has been processed with morphological functions to give Fig. 7.19.

All Sun pictures are reproduced by permission of Sun Microsystems, Inc.

From information supplied by Donna McMillan, Sun Microsystems, Inc.

For further information contact:

West U.S.A.
Sun Microsystems, Inc.
2550 Garcia Avenue
Mountain View
CA 94043
U.S.A.
Tel: 415-960-1300
Fax: 415-969-9131

United Kingdom
Sun Microsystems Europe
Bagshot Manor
Green Lane
Bagshot
Surrey GU19 5NL
U.K.

East U.S.A.
Sun Microsystems, Inc.
P.O. Box 13447
Research Triangle Park
NC 27709
U.S.A.
Tel: 919-469-8300
Email: donna.mcmillan@east.sun.com

7.7 Sterling Federal Systems, Inc.

7.7.1 FAST (Flow Analysis Software Toolkit)

Aerodynamics applications

Visualization of computational aerodynamics requires flexible, extensible, and adaptable software tools for performing analysis tasks. Full scale, 3D, unsteady, multi-zoned fluid dynamics simulations are common features of typical problems at NASA Ames' Numerical Aerodynamic Simulation (NAS). NAS scientists perform calculations on CRAY 2 and CRAY-YMP supercomputers and then graphically visualize the results on IRIS workstations. New developments in the scientific computing environment warrant a new approach to the design and implementation of analysis tools with multiple processor workstations available in the 2−8 Mflop range. FAST is a software environment for analysing such computational fluid dynamics (CFD) data.

Modular approach

The FAST environment consists of a collection of separate programs (modules) that run simultaneously. Using these modules, the NAS CFD scientist can efficiently examine the results of numerical simulations.

FAST functions

FAST provides functions which include:

- Loading data files,
- Performing calculations on the data,
- Constructing scenes of 3D graphical objects that may be animated and recorded.

Superior to earlier approaches

While these capabilities existed to some extent, they were spread across many specialized programs such as RIP, SURF, GAS and PLOT3D with overlapping functionality. These specialized programs were problematic because the data was only partially compatible, and user interfaces varied widely. The approach used in FAST solves these problems. FAST creates an environment of compatible modules, each with its own purpose and functionality. In addition, each module has a consistent, easy-to-use, highly interactive user interface (using the Panel Library developed by David Tristram, NASA, Code RNR). A programmer can add a new module to

FAST by making use of the data in shared memory, the PANEL LIBRARY interface, and the NAS (input/output) module. With these features, the FAST team has worked to make the environment as extensible as possible.

Complex fluid dynamic simulation problems created a need for new visualization techniques not possible with the existing software programs. These techniques will change as the supercomputing environment (and hence the scientific methods employed) evolve even further. Flexibility means the ability to handle a diverse range of problems. Extensibility means the ability to interact at all levels of the software hierarchy, either through existing built-in functionality or through the implementation of custom 'plug-in' modules. Adaptability means the ability to adapt to new software and hardware configurations through the use of modular structured programming methods, a graphics library standard, and common network communication protocols (like UNIX sockets) for distributed processing.

Enhanced techniques

Flexibility
Extensibility

Adaptability

For further information contact:

Sterling Federal Systems, Inc.
1121 San Antonio Avenue
Palo Alto, CA 94303, U.S.A.
Tel: 415-964-9900

7.8 Dynamic Graphics Ltd.

Interactive Volume Modeling (IVM) is a product from Dynamic Graphics, Inc., which models, displays, and interactively manipulates measured property values P in three dimensions located by X, Y, and Z.

Multi-dimensional modeling

The modeling procedure in IVM takes scattered data points of a physical property value (e.g., porosity, temperature, salinity, chemical concentration) and calculates a three-dimensional grid. This grid represents the modeled distribution of the property in three-dimensional space.

Data points

Calculation methods   The property model can be calculated by one of three methods. The first method calculates the grid throughout the volume defined by the input data distribution, or by the user. The second method restricts the calculation laterally to the area enclosed within a predefined polygon, i.e. limits in X and Y, but not in Z. The third method allows the user to specify previously calculated faulted or unfaulted two-dimensional structural surfaces as hard boundaries which limit the modeling process in X, Y, and Z. This third method enables the user to calculate, for example, a model of porosity or permeability within a zone while not allowing the model to be influenced by measured values in underlying or overlying layers. This procedure provides a much more realistic model of property variation within a zone.

3D gridding technique   The procedures for calculating property models are based on a three-dimensional extension of the robust two-dimensional gridding techniques used by Dynamic Graphics' Interactive Surface Modeling (ISM) program. These routines utilise a variation of the minimum tensions surface algorithm.

New methods   A newly developed strategy is currently being tested. This procedure is designed to enhance lateral continuity within layers. The user is given control over the degree of horizontal continuity that the gridder tried to establish. The calculated property model can be made to conform to the shape of either an underlying or overlying structural surface. The results so far have been promising, especially with thin laterally continuous or discontinuous beds.

Displaying the information   A three-dimensional grid is of limited value without display techniques that allow the user to rotate, slice, peel, and otherwise manipulate the model in real time. This rapid interactive ability is vitally important because no single view can adequately reveal the complex geometric relationships contained within any model. IVM provides these capabilities.

Display requirements   Before any manipulation can occur the user must build a display file from the three-dimensional grid. This display file is in essence the three-dimensional equivalent of a two-dimensional contour map. This file contains three-dimensional isovalue surfaces drawn at selected intervals throughout the modeled volume. These surfaces are displayed as smooth color-filled Gouraud-shaded bodies.

Once built, the user can manipulate the display file in numerous ways to better understand the internal relationships contained within the model. The model can be sliced along the X, Y or Z axes at specified intervals. The model can also be sliced first along Y, then X, then Z, or any combination thereof to produce color-filled sections along all three sides. The model may be rotated to any combination of user specified azimuth and inclination, or may be "grabbed" and turned to any desired orientation.

Understanding aspects of the model

While slicing and rotating, the user can select a particular range of isovalue surfaces to be displayed (or not displayed). For example, the user may decide to display only those porosity values between 6% and 9%, or to display all porosity values except those between 6% and 9%.

Slicing and rotating

Alternatively the user can use the "chair mode" mode display which cuts out only a piece of the model parallel to the X, Y, and Z axes. The chair void is bounded by vertical walls (X and Y axes) and a horizontal floor (Z axis) on which are displayed color-filled sections of the property distribution. The user can interactively adjust the width, depth, and height of the void along any of the axes. Also, the user can elect to display, within the chair void, a range of isovalue surfaces. These surfaces give the appearance of being extruded into the missing volume.

Chair mode

The user can also rapidly flicker between two different property models which gives the effect of superimposing the two models. The user loads one model and selects the proper orientation that best displays the property distribution. Then the other model is loaded with the same display parameters. With the touch of a single key, the user flicks between each display as rapidly or slowly as desired. This is very useful for comparing distributions of such important properties as porosity and permeability.

Superimposing models

Choice of colors   The Color Table Editor allows any combination of colors to be selected.

Analysis   IVM contains a full complement of the extensive analysis capabilities found within Dynamic Graphics' two-dimensional mapping package, ISM.

Calculating volumes   The user can calculate volumes in a variety of ways. Volume can be determined for the entire model, between isovalue surfaces, within a surface polygon, between two-dimensional structural surfaces, above and below specific depths, or any combination of these possibilities. A typical problem could be: "Calculate the pore volume between 6% and 9% porosity within Zone B inside of Lease J above the oil/water contact W".

Trend grids   Three-dimensional trend gridding is available for polynomial surfaces between 0 and 14th order. These trend grids can be subtracted from property grids to calculate three-dimensional residual surfaces. These residual grids can be used for display or volumetric calculations, if desired.

Grid operations   IVM contains three-dimensional extensions of nearly all of the standard grid operations found in two-dimensional mapping packages. A property grid can be modified through such mathematical operations as addition, subtraction, multiplication, or division by a constant or another property grid. Other grid functions are also available.

Data extraction   Data can be extracted from the three-dimensional grid in the form of individual data points or as two-dimensional grids. For individual points the user must supply X, Y and Z coordinates for the locations at which values will be back interpolated from the property model. Two-dimensional grids can be extracted either along a slice through the body, or at node locations defined by a previously calculated two-dimensional grid. The extracted two-dimensional grid values can be either the discrete back interpolated values or the column averages between two structural surfaces. The data extracted from three-dimensional grids can be used for simulation purposes, additional analyses, or for standard two-dimensional computer mapping.

IVM has been successfully used to display, verify, and edit three-dimensional seismic velocity files. IVM is being used with reservoir simulators both as a front-end processor (build and verify geometric relationships) and as a back-end processor (display and manipulate results from time steps). IVM is being used to monitor and evaluate various thermal and chemical enhanced oil recovery projects, and is being used to better understand reservoir geometries and properties.

Applications

One key area that is being studied is the distribution of permeability within a reservoir. Within certain reservoirs tilted permeability barriers have been well defined and studied. This knowledge can lead to changes in established drilling programs, and hopefully, significantly increased oil production. IVM is also used to monitor distribution and movement of pollutants within aquifers, and to assist in clean-up efforts. Concentrations of ozone within the Earth's atmosphere are being studied with IVM, as well as salinity and temperature distributions within oceans.

*Studies in
the environment*

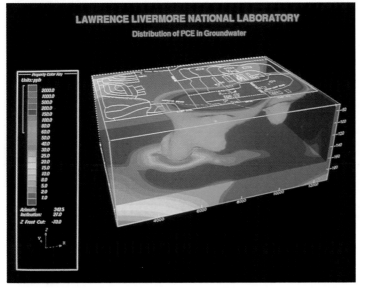

Distribution and concentration levels of PCE organic solvent contamination below a WW11 airbase site. Data from test boreholes.

*Fig. 7.20
PCE Plume*

IVM modeled and
displayed tempera-
ture data collected
for 11 years to re-
veal the higher
temperature water
from the Gulf
Stream does not
pass into the Arc-
tic Ocean.

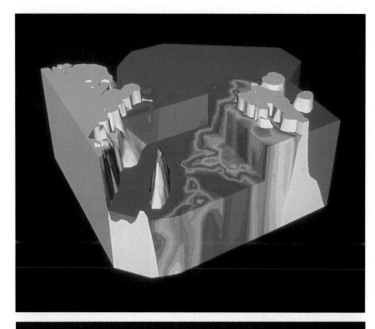

Fig. 7.21
Fram Strait –
Connecting the
Atlantic and Arctic
Oceans

IVM was used to
depict the simulat-
ed concentration
and dispersion of
pollutants in a
plume from a mu-
nicipal garbage in-
cinerator stack in
Minneapolis.

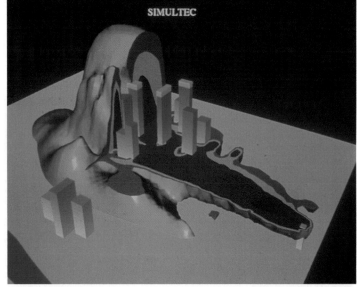

Fig. 7.22
Simulated Plume
from Smoke Stack

Geoscientists can now study and analyse three-dimensional geometric and property relationships in ways that previously have been impossible with two-dimensional mapping techniques. IVM's modeling, display, manipulation, and analysis capabilities are indeed applicable to a large number of geoscience problems.

Summary

Advantages of 3D

IVM was used to model and display porosity data from borehole readings within discrete lithologic units which were then combined into a single model. This provided a unique visualization of porosity distribution and enabled improved volumetric calculations and recovery techniques to be employed.

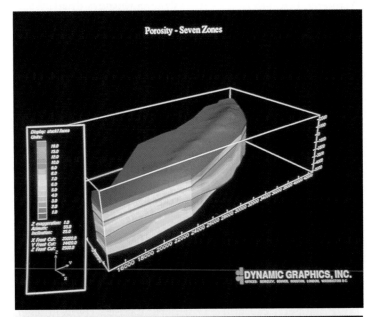

Fig. 7.23
Porosity Modeling for Oil Recovery

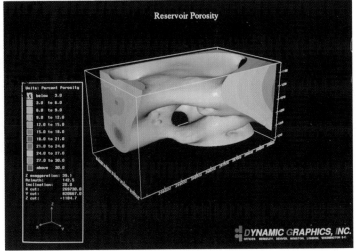

Porosity variations in a particular reservoir. Isoporosity shells are peeled back to reveal those areas with porosity greater then 6%.

Fig. 7.24
Porosity Variations

From information supplied by Peter Irwin, Dynamic Graphics Ltd.

For further information contact:

U.S.A.   United Kingdom
Dynamic Graphics, Inc.   Dynamic Graphics Ltd.
1015 Atlantic Avenue   Addison Wesley Building
Alameda, CA 94501, U.S.A.   Finchampstead Road
Tel: 415-522-0700   Wokingham
Fax: 415-522-5670   Berks RG11 2NZ, U.K.
                                                Tel: 0734-774755
                                                Fax: 0734-774721

7.9 Spyglass, Inc.

7.9.1 Spyglass Transform

Analysis and visualization

Transform is a comprehensive tool for analysis and visualization of two-dimensional data on the Macintosh. It can generate contour plots, surface plots, vector plots, line graphs, polar images, animations, overlays, and raster images (assigning colors to data values).

Data input

The Import command reads and converts 2D and 3D HDF datasets, 2D and 3D generic datasets (byte, integer, long integer, float), HDF image files, PICT files, TIFF files, FITS files, 2D ASCII data, and X-Y column data not already in array form. Transform reads 3D data one slice at a time.

Output of results

Every image, plot, or dataset can be printed to any color or black-and-white Postscript printer, or any Macintosh-compatible color printer. Exporting graphics to other Macintosh applications, or to produce 35 mm slides is easy. Data and images created in Transform can be exported as PICT or HDF files, or via the Clipboard.

7.9.2 Spyglass Dicer

Dicer is a comprehensive tool for visualizing volumetric da-   *Visualizing*
ta on the Macintosh. It can perform 3D blocks, slices in   *volume data*
three planes, 3D cubes and cutouts, variable orientation, data re-sampling, variable color maps, and animation sequences.

Dicer reads 3D HDF (float and byte), netCDF, and ge-   *Data input*
neric (byte, short and long integer, single- and double-precision floating point) file formats directly. A utility can convert and import folders of 2D files in ASCII byte, integer,
and floating-point formats, and construct 3D datasets from
the 2D files. The utility also imports 3D ASCII data files,
as well as PICT, TIFF, FITS, and HDF image files.

Dicer offers a menu of over 20 color tables, or user tables   *Color options*
can be imported. Interactive tools enable any color to be
made transparent to enable the user to 'see through' the volume it previously occupied, or to substitute colors in selected regions.

Any configuration created on screen can be saved with   *Output*
or without corresponding data, and snapshot images can be
saved alone as PICT or HDF image files. Dicer images can
be exported as PICT files using the Macintosh Clipboard,
and 2D slices can be exported to Spyglass Transform for further manipulation. Data sets can be re-sampled and saved as
either HDF or netCDF. Any image created on screen can
be printed to color (or black and white) Postscript printers,
or to Macintosh-compatible color printers.

Dicer also offers two ways to create and save animations.   *Animations*
After defining parameters, the user can generate and save sequences of 3D frames, or a sequence of 2D slices from 3D
frames created in Dicer. The sequenced images are saved in
folders and can be viewed as animations using Spyglass
View.

Information courtesy of Digital Studio.

For further information contact:

U.S.A.	United Kingdom
Spyglass, Inc.	Spyglass, c/o Digital Studio
701 Devonshire Drive, C-17	Clifton Mews
Champaign	Saffron Walden
IL 61820, U.S.A.	Essex CB10 1EE, U.K.
Tel: 217-355-1665	Tel: 0799-513773
Fax: 217-398-0413	Fax: 0799-513454

7.10 LightWork Design Ltd.

High-quality images

LightWorks is a powerful new image generation system from LightWork Design Ltd. that enables users of modeling software to create high-quality images of their models, showing accurate surface finishes and lighting effects. It is optimised for interactive operation in computer-aided design environments.

Natural phenomena

Images of photographic quality are produced by simulating natural phenomena such as reflective surfaces, transparency and shadows from any number of light sources. Arbitrarily complex material characteristics can be defined to create realistic finishes such as marble, wood, brick, chrome and steel. A wide range of geometric modeling primitives are supported on to which scanned images can be mapped.

Applications

LightWorks can be used in many application areas. Examples are visualization for product designers; visualizing simulation data for scientists and engineers; building designs for architects; accurate simulations of color and lighting schemes for interior designers; print and animation for graphic designers.

User interface

The system has an interactive mouse and window-based scene editor module which presents an easy-to-use yet powerful user interface with which the visual characteristics of a model can be controlled. Incremental rendering techniques enable many color and lighting combinations to be compared in a short time.

Fig. 7.25
Engineering
Component

This engineering component shows different kinds of metal surfaces – the machined chrome, the cast red, and the threads. The "bumps" on the background and also on the red surface are done by displacements. Lighting and shadows are also present.

Fig. 7.26
Architectural
Application

An example of an architectural application. This shows different finishes, soft shadows, and a perspective view.

Written in C, LightWorks has been designed to be easily ported across a wide variety of computer platforms including UNIX workstations, MS-DOS PCs, and cost-effective parallel processing computers. LightWorks is supported on Sun-4/SPARC, IBM RISC System/6000, Silicon Graphics IRIS/4D, Hewlett Packard 9000 300/400/700/800, Sony NEWS, and 80386 and 80486 IBM PC compatibles running MS-DOS with Phar Lap's 386/Dos-Extender or Microsoft's Windows 3.0.

Information supplied by Dr R. Gordon Oliver, LightWork Design Ltd.

For further information contact:

Lightwork Design Ltd.
Sheffield Science Park
Arundel Street
Sheffield S1 2NS, U.K.
Tel: 0742-724126
Fax: 0742-720379

7.11 Ricoh Company Ltd.
Use of Visualization in Modeling
and CAD/CAM

Representing
3D shapes

Solid modelers, designed to represent 3D shapes as solids, have become essential tools in computer-aided design and manufacturing (CAD/CAM) systems. The benefits of solid modelers vary from designing to molding, and from structural analysis to robot simulations. Unlike surface modelers, however, existing solid modelers have had limitations in the representation of complex surfaces.

3D modeling

DESIGNBASE is a 3D solid modeling system developed by Ricoh Company Ltd. This is designed to represent complex free-form surfaces in UNIX workstation environments. Using a surface representation method called the "Gregory patch", DESIGNBASE enables free-form surfaces to be smoothly connected and locally operated.

Fig. 7.27
Scene produced
by DESIGNBASE

DESIGNBASE provides various surface representation methods: the Gregory patch, the rational boundary Gregory patch, natural quadric surfaces (spheres, cylinders, cones), and n-th degree rational Bezier patches. Featured with these surface representation methods and translation libraries, DESIGNBASE is capable of bi-directional data exchange with other CAD/CAM systems. DESIGNBASE translates its surface data to non-uniform rational B-splines (NURBS), the de facto standard surface representation method, and sends the data through Initial Graphic Exchange Specification (IGES) to other CAD/CAM systems.

Surface representation

The Gregory patch is the more suitable surface representation method for the smooth connection of free-form surfaces compared to the Bezier patch. A bicubic Gregory patch, which is defined by 20 control points, is an extension of the bicubic Bezier patch, which has 16 control points.

Connecting surfaces smoothly

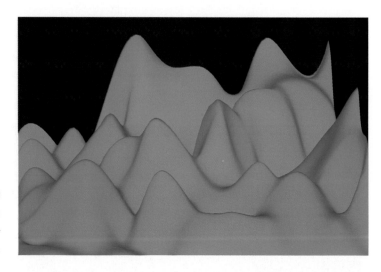

Fig. 7.28
Free-form Surface
represented by
Gregory Patch

The extra 4 internal control points of the Gregory patch are used in the smooth connection of surfaces and enable the interpolation of irregular meshes.

Fig. 7.29
Irregular Mesh
represented by
Rational Boundary
Gregory Patch–1

Fig. 7.30
Irregular Mesh
represented by
Rational Boundary
Gregory Patch–2

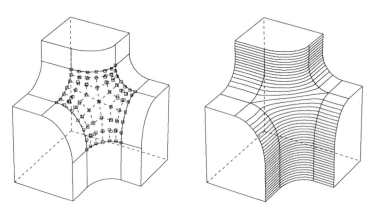

Figure 7.29 shows the control points of the rational boundary Gregory patch. A six-sided irregular mesh is interpolated by 6 RBG patches.

In Figure 7.30 the contour lines show the smoothness of this surface representation method.

Fillets   Filleting is a crucial capability for CAD software for designing products such as automobile engines or electric appliances.

Boolean operations (union, difference, and intersection) are critical in the representation of complex shapes. However, most solid modeling systems approximate the shape of the free-form surfaces with facets when executing these operations.

Boolean operations

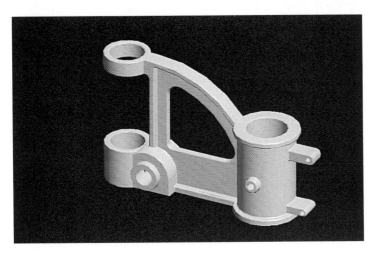

Fig. 7.31 Engineering Component created by applying Boolean Operations

When natural quadric surfaces are intersecting, DESIGNBASE uses a special library for high-speed surface-to-surface intersection calculations.

This shows an example of a body generated by applying Boolean operations. The geometric accuracy of the resultant solid based on these operations is within the margin of 10^{-6} on intersection vertices and 10^{-3} on intersection curves.

To support the trial and error implicit in the design process, DESIGNBASE provides high-speed Undo, Redo and Re-execution commands. Each command of DESIGNBASE is subdivided internally into primitive operations, and each primitive operation has a reverse operation. By executing the reverse operations, previous shapes can be generated by tracing the tree-type history backwards (Undo) and forward (Redo). In addition, shapes input previously can be modified easily by giving different parameter values (Re-execution); this facility is useful for designing analogous shapes.

Trial and error in the design process

Summary   Computer-aided design (CAD) began with 2D systems which replaced drafting instruments. However, total CAD/CAM or computer-aided engineering (CAE) systems require the facility to process 3D data, and it must be possible to freely exchange this data between systems.

Solid modeling systems are assuming a more significant role as industry introduces CAD/CAM/CAE systems. High powered workstations enable such systems to perform efficiently and also cost-effectively.

Applications   DESIGNBASE has been applied to the automobile and electricity industries as the basis of CAD/CAM/CAE requirements. It has also been used for rendering, stereo lithography, and pre-processing for the production of finite element meshes.

Reference

Chiyokura H.: *Solid Modeling with DESIGNBASE: Theory and Implementation*. Addison Wesley, Reading, MA, 1988.

Information supplied by T. Ito, A. O'Neill, and H. Toriya, Ricoh Company Ltd.

For further information contact:

Ricoh Company Ltd.
1-1-17 Koishikawa
Bunkyo-ku
Tokyo 112
Japan
Tel: 81-3-3815-7261
Fax: 81-3-3818-0348

7.12 Vital Images, Inc.

Vital Images began developing software as part of a research *VoxelView*
project at Maharishi International University to visualize la-
ser-scan confocal microscope data of living nerve cells. This
research was funded by Iowa Department of Economic Development and the National Science Foundation.

VoxelView is a general purpose, high-performance volume rendering package. Data values of voxels can be mapped to corresponding opacity values. This enables the user
to view faint or small details inside the volume. It is also
possible to do thresholding to remove voxels, or redistribute
voxel values from one range to another. Sequences of renderings can be stored and then played back in real time. The
following features are also included:

- graphical data base system,
- full surface shading with lighting,
- user control of animation parameters,
- gradient operations to extract and selectively display
  nested surfaces within the volume,
- autoconfiguring for multiprocessor systems.

VoxelLab is an entry-level version of VoxelView and is avail- *VoxelLab*
able on the Silicon Graphics workstation. It enables beginning users to appreciate the power and potential of volume
rendering systems.

For further information contact:

Vital Images, Inc.
P. O. Box 551
Fairfield
IO 52556
U. S. A.
Tel: 515-472-7726
Fax: 515-472-1661

Chapter 8
Current Public Domain Systems in Use

Readers are recommended to read Chapter 4 for a classification and categorisation of scientific visualization systems before reading this present chapter. Chapter 4 sets out the overall framework into which the products outlined in Chapters 7 and 8 fit.

In addition, readers should note the points on public domain systems that are set out in Chapter 4 (Section 4.4).

Contact addresses are provided for each product at the end of each section.

8.1 Khoros

Khoros is an open environment for data processing, visualization, and software development. This summary describes how the Khoros software system can be utilized as a foundation or platform to improve productivity and promote software reuse in data processing applications. First, a high-level description of Khoros is given, then the current status of Khoros is discussed.

8.1.1 Overview

Tool for research and development

The Khoros system integrates multiple user interface modes, code generators, instructional aids, data visualization, and information processing. The result is a comprehensive tool for computational research and development. The Khoros infrastructure consists of five major subsystems:

- a general visual language,
- a user-interface development system (UIDS),

- an interoperable data exchange format (viff),
- application-specific data processing libraries,
- interactive data display/manipulation programs and a visualization toolkit.

The software structure that embodies this system provides for extensibility and portability, and allows for easy tailoring to target specific application domains and processing environments. Khoros is a successful example of how research programming, end-user applications programming, information processing, data visualization, instruction, documentation, and maintenance can be integrated to build a state-of-the-art software environment.

Portable and extensible

8.1.2 Subsystem Component Descriptions

a) X Windows Applications

The interactive graphical user interface programs are based on MIT X11R4 and the Athena widgets. They are all designed to have a simple and consistent look and feel.

Program Name	Description
cantata	extensible visual programming language
editimage	interactive image display and manipulation
animate	interactive image sequence display
xprism2 and xprism3	comprehensive 2D and 3D plotting packages
viewimage	surface visualization (imagery draped over elevation data)
warpimage	image registration and warping
concert	distributed user interface controller

b) Visual Language

Dataflow graphs

The visual language of Khoros, cantata, is a graphically expressed, dataflow-oriented language. The user builds a cantata application program by connecting processing nodes to form a dataflow graph. Nodes are selected from an application specific library of routines created using the Khoros UIDS, and may have arbitrary granularity, from fine to large grain. Control nodes and a parser extend the functionality of the underlying data flow methodology. Visual procedures, representing a hierarchy of subgraphs, add structure to the visual language and help to manage the complexity often associated with visual programming. A dynamic execution scheduler allows the user to interactively execute the entire flow graph across a heterogeneous computer network. The execution can be set to either a demand-driven or data-driven model depending on the application and desired level of interactivity.

Many applications

Cantata has been targeted at a variety of application domains: a visual language interface has been completed for the LINPACK/EISPACK libraries, an image processing library, a digital signal processing library and a remote sensing/geographical information system. The design of cantata promotes code reuse and modular design of libraries.

c) User Interface Development System

The Khoros system combines interactive graphical user interface specification/editing and code generation to give the user a programmer's assistant. This UIDS can be used to create general X Windows applications or to extend cantata.

Dialog

The central component of the UIDS is a high-level user interface specification that represents a formal description of the dialog between the user and the application, independent of the user interface mode. The specification is used directly to generate the code for either a graphical or command-line user interface. When the user interface specification is combined with a formal Khoros program specification, the entire application (documentation and code) can be maintained via a set of automated source configuration tools.

The software development tools that are provided allow an end-user to act as a developer to extend the system.

Program Name	Description
preview	graphical user interface display tool
composer	interactive graphical user interface editor
conductor	code generation tool for a graphical user interface
ghostwriter	code generation tool for a command line user interface
kinstall	source configuration and management tool

The user interfaces created with the Khoros UIDS all utilize the same layered libraries. This provides features common to all applications, such as: *User interfaces*

- journal recording and playback,
- distributed user interface,
- reconfigurability without recompiling,
- consistency of use.

Perhaps the most powerful and innovative item in the list is the distributed user interface or groupware capability. All of the graphical user interfaces created within the Khoros system allow for multiple user interfaces to be running on different machines. This allows a group of researchers (either as master and slaves or as all masters) to simultaneously interact across a network using the same data and application software. This groupware capability motivates users to share resources.

The UIDS also promotes consistent structured programming methodology and styles as well as code reuse. The hope is that as Khoros evolves, many reusable libraries can be provided in various languages for various applications that have a consistent and powerful user interface.

d) Interoperable Data Exchange

Data formats The Khoros data structure or visualization model supports general geometric objects, multidimensional data, and a robust mapping scheme. Storage type conversion between different architecture platforms is automatically performed by the read/write utilities, i.e., DEC VAX floating-point data is automatically converted to IEEE format if read on a SUN computer. The consistent use of the Khoros data structure promotes an algorithm library that can be used in many disciplines and supports data sharing.

Standard formats It is important to state that as Khoros expands, there will be a need to support a set of "standard" file formats. Currently, Khoros provides for data interchange with other systems via file format converters. Khoros supports the following file formats: TIFF, pbm, BIG, DEM, DLG, ELAS, FITS, Matlab, sun raster, TGA, and xbm.

e) Data Processing Libraries

Functions Khoros includes a library of programs that can operate on point data, one-dimensional data, two-dimensional data and multiband or vector data. These operators are designed to be polymorphic, i.e., they function on bit, byte, short, integer, float and complex data types. This also implies that the functions will operate differently depending on the dimensionality of the data.

Interface levels There are two interface levels defined in the library levels functions in Khoros; the program or process interface and the function call or procedure interface. The program interface is determined completely by the high-level user interface specification described above. The procedure interface is currently not as well defined, but allows the procedures (functions) to be easily combined into a single program. Visual programs are built by executing a set of programs using the program interface.

The library contains over 260 programs, in the following categories: arithmetic, classification, color conversion, data conversion, file format conversion, feature extraction, frequency filtering, spatial filtering, morphology filtering, geometric manipulation, histogram manipulation, statistics, signal generation, linear operations, segmentation, spectral estimation, subregion, and transforms.

Library programs

f) Visualization Toolkit

A visualization tool is of limited utility if it cannot be modified to view and process data in a new user-specified way. This will only be possible if the user can modify and extend the software system. A scientist should not be required to modify a large C program to do this; a high-level language or specification should be provided as in the Khoros UIDS.

Adapt and extend

Khoros includes generic interactive X Windows applications for image (2D data) visualization and three-dimensional surface rendering. But more important are the high-level graphics and display libraries that are accessible from the UIDS to build custom visualization programs. The following libraries act as a visualization toolkit that is layered on top of Xlib, Xtk and the Athena Widgets.

High-level tools

Library Name	Description
forms	hierarchical user interface based on forms and panes
utils	browsers, error reporting, pop-up lists, and help
graphics	2D and 3D drawing library; supports X, Postscript, HPGL
display	image display and editing; manages color allocation and editing

8.1.3 Current Status of Khoros

Many users   The Khoros user community is applying Khoros primarily to image and signal processing research and development projects. In addition, sites are retargeting Khoros to application domains such as, three-dimensional volume rendering, relational databases, and telecommunications. Khoros is being used as a teaching tool at several universities.

Help   The documentation for the system is a combination of on-line help and printed manuals. The manual comprises 2200 pages in three separate volumes: User's Manual, Programmer's Manual, and Reference Guide. Also, journal playback files are provided to give the new user "live" demonstrations of the various applications.

Platforms   Khoros currently runs on SUN, DEC, APOLLO/HP, SGI, IBM, NeXT, and CRAY platforms and there are porting efforts for 386/486 and Apple platforms. Khoros is now available via anonymous ftp at no charge, or a tape and printed documentation can be ordered for $250.00. Hundreds of Khoros users participate in a mail user's group, email khoros-request@chama.eece.unm.edu for more information. The software can be obtained on tape by mail or by ftp. Email khoros-request for an order form, or mail the request to the address below. Orders can also be faxed to 505-277-1439.

The ftp address for the software is pprg.eece.unm.edu (129.24.24.10).
   Login: anonymous (or ftp)
   Password: user__name@machine
   cd /pub/khoros

For users in Germany, the ftp is ftp.uni-erlangen.de
   Login: anonymous
Password: user__name@machine
   cd /cyber/khoros

The documentation can also be printed by using the "prnmanual" program.

In Figure 8.1, the cantata visual language is being used for two simple applications: blending two images and then pseudo-coloring (top), enhancing a magnetic resonance image of a human spine (bottom).

In Figure 8.2 the cantata visual language program is used to synthesize, filter, and display a one-dimensional signal.

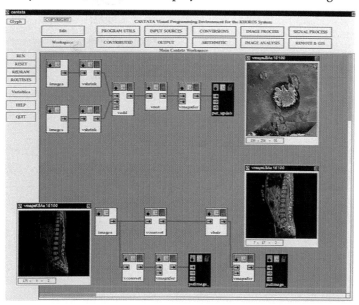

Fig. 8.1
Cantata Visual
Language

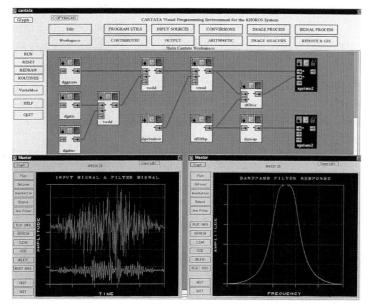

Fig. 8.2
Filter and Display

The left xprism2 plots shows the signal before and after filtering and the right xprism2 plot shows the filter response.

The three-dimensional scientific data plotting package xprism3 can be used to interactively visualize surfaces, contours, and meshes (Figure 8.3).

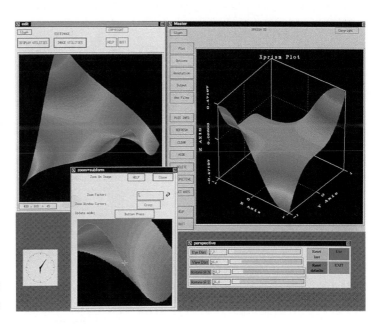

Fig. 8.3
3D Capabilities

The Khoros system can be used to integrate satellite imagery with ground elevation and map data to produce a three-dimensional scene of the earth's surface. The viewimage program is used to interactively change the perspective view of the surface, and the animate application can be used to create a 'fly-by' sequence (Figure 8.4).

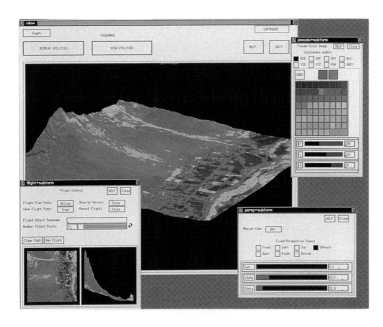

Fig. 8.4
Integration
Methods

Warpimage is an interactive application for registering and then warping images to produce integrated data sets (Figure 8.5).

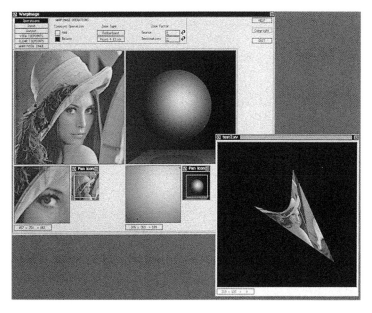

Fig. 8.5
Image Warping

The cantata visual language is being used to remove shot noise from an image of the moon. This is done by using a count loop containing a median filter (Figure 8.6).

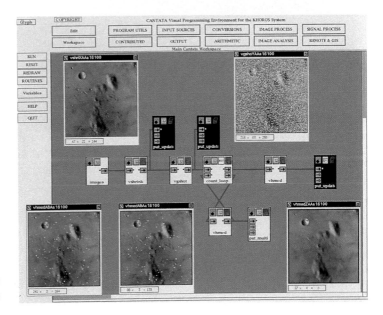

Fig. 8.6
Noise Removal

Contributed by Dr. John Rasure, University of New Mexico.

For further information contact:

The Khoros Group
Department of Electrical and Computer Engineering
University of New Mexico
Albuquerque
NM 87131
U.S.A.
Fax: 505-277-1439.
Email queries: khoros-request@chama.eece.unm.edu

8.2 apE: A Dataflow Toolkit for Scientific Visualization

In 1984, the Ohio State University competed with institutions across the United States to host a National Supercomputer Center. While its proposal was highly ranked, Ohio State lost its bid for National Science Foundation funding to obtain a center. However, the highly motivated group of computational chemists who spearheaded Ohio State's chemistry efforts then received help from the state. In 1987, the legislature appropriated funds for the Ohio Board of Regents' supercomputer initiative to create a center serving academic and industrial users in the state of Ohio. In June 1987, a Cray X-MP was installed at the Ohio Supercomputer Center, followed by a Cray Y-MP in June 1989.

Background

Computational chemistry

One of the early supporters of the Ohio Supercomputer Center was Professor Charles Csuri, a pioneer in the field of computer graphics and Director of the Advanced Computing Center for the Arts and Design at Ohio State. He foresaw the rise of scientific visualization in the early 1980s and built a significant graphics research component into the base of the then-fledgling Ohio Supercomputer Center. Thus in late 1987, the newly formed Ohio Supercomputer Graphics Project set out to design an effective software system for visualization, apE.

Developments in computer graphics

Tools for supercomputers

Rather than dictate to the scientific community a particular methodology, extensive time was spent with potential users to understand the real needs of scientific research. The apE group listened to users of all kinds of current graphics software and hardware, discovered the realities of fixed budgets that permit only modest hardware acquisition and the effects of slow network connections on high speed computing. In short, they tried to face the real world, and to design and build a product that would outlast current hardware platforms while providing a high degree of flexibility to today's users.

What do potential users really need from computers?

Hardware independence and flexibility

Dataflow model

Efforts in the mid-1980s at the Computer Graphics Research Group (now known as the Advanced Computing Center for the Arts and Design) at the Ohio State University led to selection of a dataflow model for the apE system.

Steps in understanding scientific data

A dataflow system maps very well to the general steps followed in visualizing scientific data. Most researchers follow a five-step process, beginning with a computational or experimental simulation, and concluding with interpretation. Intermediate steps include preparation, mapping, and rendering (the preparation stage is occasionally omitted or merged with the map stage). Ideally, the results of interpre-

Feedback

tation can be fed back into the original experiment or simulation. This kind of feedback is known as steering, and has been used with great success in some limited applications. New software technology, beyond the reach of apE, is needed to investigate the steering issue completely.

Utilizing networked computers

The dataflow abstraction is ideal for remote execution and parallel operation. Network computing environments are commonplace, and distributed computation is a requirement for maximum resource utilization. Dataflow systems can naturally distribute each execution element on a separate machine or processor. The apE dataflow is data-driven and not demand-driven, which offers the benefit of parallel execution for time-dependent or multi-frame data sets. Each element operates not under the control of some central authority but instead only as input data, frame boundaries,

Local and centralized computers

and other local conditions dictate. Successive elements in a visualization pipeline can be operating on separate groups of data, all in concert, without any additional user interaction. This notion of distributed computing maps well to the realities encountered among researchers, as they are often located at distant sites, far from their supercomputing resource, but may have some local computing power available.

Dataflow language

Once the group was firmly committed to the data flow concept, they examined the requirements for a data language. Incompatible binary formats are common in a heterogeneous network environment. While transmission of data as text files would mitigate this problem, the operational overhead for such transmission was out of the question in an interactive system. Thus a dataflow language was born, designed to represent not only common data elements from the scientific domain (such as grids and variables) but also common graphical forms, such as objects, images, and geometries.

Representing data elements and graphical forms

There is a great difference between writing a small piece of personal software and constructing a large software environment. Additional complexity appears when consideration is given to machine and device independence and portability. Still more demands come from software which is to be distributed not as a closed system but as source code, to be modified, improved, and extended as required. The group tried to build as portable a graphics environment as is possible using existing software and hardware technology. Clearly, the analysis of this requirement results in a different answer today than it did in 1987 when this project was begun. However, many of the design decisions faced then are also faced today by large scale developers. These decisions can be summarized as three primary turning points: the selection of an operating system, the selection of a graphics library, and the selection of a user interface.

Software engineering principles

Extensibility by users

Portability

Design decisions

The apE system is built on the UNIX platform. The mid-1980s saw an explosive growth in a new breed of personal computer known as the "workstation". Performance, power, and software resources that were once only part of large mainframe systems rapidly became available on the desktop, and the UNIX operating system quickly became the de facto standard operating system. Manufacturers that did not respond to this trend saw their sales diminish.

UNIX platform

De facto standard

The group chose not to embed any graphics library in the basis of the system. They were criticized for not building their software upon a graphics software layer such as CORE, GKS, PHIGS, PHIGS+, PEX, or others. In late 1987, when this decision was made, the number of competing standards was large, and no clear winner had emerged. None of the standards available then were really sufficient for scientific visualization. Constructing the software on

Independent of graphics libraries

Proliferating standards

Visualization requirements

Add-on costs for graphics libraries

such a platform would be a tacit endorsement of one of these standards and would require users to obtain the necessary licenses to actually program within apE. Most workstation vendors do not currently ship a PHIGS product, for example, as no-cost, bundled software with their systems, so additional cost is incurred in purchasing, installing, and maintaining a graphics library in addition to apE. All that is needed to run apE is apE.

Independent of window systems

apE incorporates a new interface layer on top of existing "standards". The group chose not to build upon one of the existing window systems. Clearly today the only "standard" window system is the X Window System. However, in 1987, a number of alternative threatened to steal the glory from X. Despite the claims, the intense battle between such competing higher-level standards as Motif and Openlook will continue this uncertainty.

Motif and Openlook

Developing the software

With source code control, interface, and (lack of) a graphics library in hand, the group was ready to implement the application software. This phase of the development was divided into three logical elements: the construction of the libraries, the construction of the individual dataflow elements (or modules), and finally the construction of the tools and interface that would comprise the look and feel of apE to the average user. The library implementation was done in phases, with the UNIX-level hiding functions completed first. The data language, user interface library, and graphics functions were done in preliminary test forms prior to full implementation. The resulting test software was released (as version 1.1) and used to help motivate the full implementation of apE version 2.0.

User interface

Look and feel

First version

Version 1.1 of apE, released in early 1989, had many of the important aspects of the dataflow design, but lacked the full implementation needed to make a truly useful software package. Many changes occurred in the 18 months from the public release of apE 1.1 to the first glimpses of apE 2.0.

Data language extensions

The data language "flow" that had been developed for apE was enhanced, extended, and rechristened flux. Specifically designed to deal with large amounts of data in user-de-

signed grouping, flux is a powerful information management tool. All data entities, from images to variables to pipeline descriptions to icons, are represented in the flux.

Flux

The generic user interface, first presented in apE 1.1, was
expanded and renamed face. The face libraries provide a
complete, window-system-independent interface for program development. Face elements include most of the standard interface items, such as buttons, menus, sliders, scan-
ners, and text entry boxes. On top of this layer more complex elements are provided as well, such as alerts, browsers
(for selecting a text element from a list), and collectors (for
selecting several text elements from a list). Face provides a
generic, application-based interface for interactive tool design which allows a single application to execute under Sun-
View, X, and GL without significant source code changes.

*Advances in the
user interface*

Face elements

*Interworking with
SunView X, GL*

The operational tools provided in the first release were
also significantly reworked. The pipeline construction tool
has been reworked to increase interactivity and to handle
different connection methods between the elements (apE
1.1 used UNIX pipes to connect the dataflow elements; apE
2.0 uses both UNIX pipes and sockets for connections). A
central console provides an outlet for error messages and access to documentation. An interactive image viewer allows
manipulation of single and multiple images and real-time
"playback" of image sequences. A geometry viewer allows
interactive viewing of geometries.

Operational tools

Pipelines

Errors and help

*Playback of
sequences*

While apE 1.1 was limited to nearly-linear pipelines, apE
2.0 is designed to allow complex pipeline configurations, including multi-input and multi-output and cyclic graphics.
This cyclic capability provides apE 2.0 users with the ability
to investigate connections between graphics and supercomputer simulations, and to attempt to "steer" a simulation
through visual feedback. These additions are all natural extensions of apE 1.1.

Complex pipelines

*Supercomputer
simulations*

Finally, the filters/modules have been extended to include three-dimensional elements as well as the traditional
two-dimensional elements found in the first release of apE.

3D element filters

Visualization techniques

Visualization techniques include carpet and contour plots, surface detection, terrain generation, and all forms of rendering from scanline polygonal techniques to ray tracing. A

Volume methods

volumetric rendering system based on methods methods developed by Levoy is also included. Particle tracing, advection, and surface feature detection (such as stream lines) are also included. In addition, full prototypes are provided to al-

Extensions

low extension of the system by the addition of new filters, data types, tools, and interface elements.

Distribution policy

One of the real keys to the success of the apE software effort has been the distribution policy. While a corporation must be concerned about profits, competition, market anal-

Criteria for success

ysis, and other factors, the group concentrated solely on providing the best tools for the research community, knowing that success would be judged by user productivity, not the corporate bottom line. The best and only result hoped for was widespread usage and increased productivity among Ohio's researchers.

Release of code

The first version of apE was released in binary form only. For many users this was insufficient, because it prevented them from fully utilizing the software. First, many people

Modifications

needed to modify the code to suit particular needs or demands in a particular application or field of interest. Some

Changes

needed to make changes to suit local equipment or configurations. Finally, for many, not being able to see the source code caused a lack of confidence in the final results. Even if the code is not modified, it is of great value to examine

Understanding

sections to understand how a particular function is implemented or why an unexpected result is seen. University environments typically enjoy source code for most applications for precisely this reason.

Source code availability

The group can now distribute the second version of the software in source code form. All of the apE system, including window system layers, program development layers, data format layers, and all existing filters and tools will be released in source code form with the software. Academic institutions can request this software (with manuals) at no charge, although a license (prohibiting redistribution) must be signed.

For commercial and non-profit users, the university has chosen to pursue commercialization of the software with the TaraVisual Corporation in Columbus, Ohio. This company offers maintenance, installation, and consulting services related to apE. It is not affiliated in any way with the Ohio State University or the developers of apE and thus the version of apE offered through TaraVisual is expected to diverge from that offered by OSU. While this may seem counter to some of the philosophies of apE, it was a decision made by the university and is not representative of the general feelings of the developers. *Commercial users*

The apE system does not represent a breakthrough in computer graphics. Most of the technology that has been harnessed to construct apE has been in existence for a number of years, and precious little of it could in any way be considered to be state of the art. However, the apE system does represent a significant new step in placing sophisticated tools into the hands of users. The project has helped to push industry toward a greater realization of the nature of the scientific visualization problem. The potential of visual methods for data analysis is enormous, and we need to recognize that the grand challenge that faces us today is not in making faster silicon but in finding new ways to improve the productivity of our research community. *Aggregation of existing tools and methodologies* *Tools for real users* *Power of visual methods*

apE Runs on Convex C-1, C-2, Cray, SGI, SUN, HP, NeXT, DEC, Stardent, and IBM (RS6000, AIX). *Platforms*

apE supports data manipulation, data mapping, image rendering, and animation. Data manipulation includes a data flow language (flux), creation and editing of polygonal data, image format conversion, image processing, and image labelling. Data mapping includes isosurface construction of volumetric data, support for RGB, HSV, HLS colorspace mapping, color palette editing, data in uniform and non-uniform grids, rectangular, polar, spherical and geocentric coordinate systems in 2, 3, and n dimensions. *Summary of facilities*

The user interface supports SunView, X Window System, and Silicon Graphics GL. It has a visual language paradigm, and fully indexed on-line user documentation. It also allows distributed processing over a computer network. *User interfaces*

Image rendering   Image rendering includes 1D frequency plots, 2D contour line images, 2D continuous-color contour images, 2D colour contours with gradient shading (bump mapping), carpet plots, photorealistic rendering of polygonal data, volume rendering, particle animation of vector fields, and "glyph" rendering.

Reference   "A Dataflow Toolkit for Visualization" by Scott Dyer in
information   IEEE Computer Graphics and Applications, Vol. 10, No. 4, 1990, pp. 60–69, gives further information on apE.

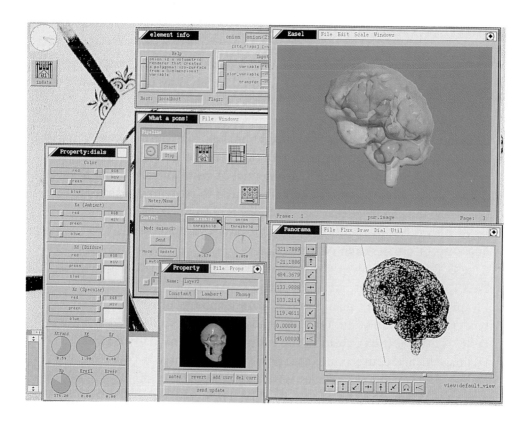

Fig. 8.7   Isosurface rendering using apE. A pipeline has been cre-
Isosurface   ated to examine a 3D volumetric dataset consisting of MRI
Rendering   data from a human subject. Two isosurface values have been selected – the outer one has been made transparent.

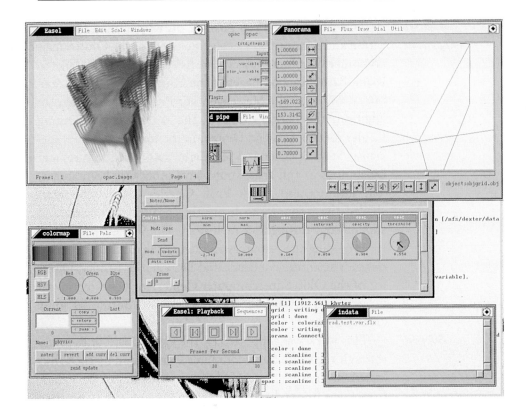

Volumetric rendering using apE. A pipeline has been cre- *Fig. 8.8*
ated to examine a 3 D dataset of temperature in the Atlantic *Volume Rendering*
Ocean and has been rendered using a ray-tracing technique.

Acknowl-
edgements   This project has been possible only because of the dedi-
cation and commitment of the members of the Ohio Supercomputer Graphics Project. The listed authors would like to
thank Barb Dean, Manager of the Ohio Visualization Laboratory, and Michelle Messenger, our Project Coordinator. In
addition, the participation of the Advanced Computing
Center for the Arts and Design, in the form of graphics specialists Steve Spencer and Jeff Light, has added features and
capabilities to apE that would have otherwise been absent.
The authors also thank Prof. Charles Csuri, who mar-
shalled the resources to bring this project into being and
supported it throughout its history, Dr. William McCurdy,
for providing the resources and being the catalyst for many
of apE's scientific concepts, and Dr. Charlie Bender, Director of the Ohio Supercomputer Center, for believing in the
project, and continuing to supporting it, during its most
crucial hours.

Support   This work was supported by the Ohio Board of Regents,
through the Ohio Supercomputer Center, and by the Ohio
State University. This work was supported in part by a grant
from Cray Research, Inc., by an equipment grant from Apple Computer, Inc., and by an equipment loan from Silicon
Graphics, Inc.

Contributed by the Ohio Supercomputer Graphics Project:

Scott Dyer, Project Leader
Steve Anderson
John Berton
Pete Carswell
John Donkin
Jeff Faust
Jill Kempf
Robert Marshall

Since this information was submitted, apE has been taken
over by TaraVisual Corporation, who are now responsible
for its distribution and support. Although it was initially
made available as a public domain product from Ohio Su-

percomputer Center, this is no longer the case at the time of writing. However, discounts on the software are available for academic use. All enquiries on apE should now be directed to the address below, and not to Ohio Supercomputer Center.

TaraVisual Corporation
929 Harrison Avenue
Columbus
OH 43215
U.S.A.
Tel: (800) 458-8731
Tel: 614-291-2912
Fax: 614-291-2867

8.3 National Center for Supercomputing Applications (NCSA)

The NCSA Tools for the Macintosh

The National Center for Supercomputing Applications (NCSA) offers a number of tools that are available in the public domain. NCSA Distributed DataScope is an interactive data analysis tool that displays 32-bit scientific data values in spreadsheet form or as simple scaled, interpolated, or polar color raster images. NCSA Image is a color imaging and analysis application that permits manipulation of two- and three-dimensional image data sets. Distributed capabilities across TCP/IP network connections allow image processing on powerful computers such as a CRAY 1. Specific data manipulation features in NCSA Image include histogram equalizations, contrast enhancements, and useful utility functions. NCSA Layout is a presentation tool that allows the and user to display and annotate two-dimensional data annotation images so that users can photograph their Macintosh screen display with a 35 mm camera and produce presentation-quality slides. NCSA Telnet provides a link be-

Interactive data analysis

Color imaging and analysis

Layout and annotation

File transfer tween the Macintosh and the TCP/IP networks. It includes a standard file transfer server (FTP), which allows file sharing with other machines.

All these tools are available free via the Internet. The software and documentation are also available for purchase through the NCSA Technical Resources Catalog.

Contact:
NCSA Documentation Orders
152 Computing Applications Building
605 East Springfield Avenue
Champaign, IL 61820, U.S.A.
Tel: 217-244-0072.
(This information is supplied courtesy of visualization Technology: an Introduction", by Anne Kaplan-Neher, in Syllabus, Summer 1991, Number 17, P.O. Box 2716, Sunnyvale, CA 94087- 0716, AppleLink: SYLLABUS, Internet: SYLLABUS@APPLELINK.APPLE.COM; Phone and Fax: 408-773-0670. It was initially obtained from the "Articles database of CCNEWS, the Electronic Forum for Campus Computing Newsletter Editors, a BITNET-based service of EDUCOM").

8.4 GPLOT, DRAWCGM, P3D (Pittsburgh Supercomputer Center)

GPLOT can interpret CGM metafiles and can run animation hardware. DRAWCGM produces rasters from 2D arrays of integers or reals. P3D creates and views 3D models. Such models can be viewed on SUNs and SGIs. It can build isosurface models and molecular models, and create animations directly on video tape. It is available via anonymous FTP from calpe.psc.edu. Further information is given below.

8.4.1 The GPLOT CGM Interpreter

The Pittsburgh Supercomputing Center began in 1986 as *Supercomputer*
one of several sites charged by the U.S. National Science *center*
Foundation with providing supercomputer (and other) capabilities to NSF researchers. Unlike other such sites, the user base (over 2000 researchers) is very diverse, both geo-
graphically and technologically, with almost all users physi- *Remote access*
cally remote.

Providing a graphical capability to these users was prob- *Graphics*
lematic; but being a new center provided the option to de- *standards*
sign systems from scratch. It was decided to standardise
completely on the Computer Graphics Metafile (CGM) for- *CGM*
mat for two-dimensional image storage. Accordingly only
graphics packages that could produce CGM files were pur-
chased. Each of these packages came with a CGM translator,
but it was found that these translators could only reliably
translate CGM files from the corresponding graphics pack- *Which CGM?*
age!

It was unacceptable to distinguish between types of
CGM files and it was decided to write a CGM translator:
GPLOT. In addition to homogenizing the CGM file popu- *GPLOT*
lation there were several other advantages to using this software. Firstly, GPLOT could be freely distributed to remote *Distributed*
sites and users were encouraged to produce their CGM files *software*
at the PSC and ship them home for viewing with a local copy of GPLOT. This improved response for the users dramat-
ically compared to viewing the CGM files across their net- *Reduced*
work connection and also reduced the load on the network *network load*
connections. Secondly it allowed the rapid addition of new
output devices and facilities.

GPLOT was more successful than expected; there are *275 sites*
now over 275 sites on the list of users, including most of the
major universities and research laboratories in the USA and
several sites in other countries. GPLOT now supports output to many different output devices with three different user interfaces.

Video

Frame checking

GPLOT was also used to greatly facilitate the creation of videos by remote users. Users are encouraged to create CGM files with many (possibly very many) frames. They can examine individual frames at their home site using their copy of GPLOT and when satisfied with their "look" submit them for animation. A local copy of GPLOT at the PSC is then used to create a full animation either on a Sony Umatic recorder or on a Sony laser disk recorder. It can then be dubbed to VHS tape and mailed to the user, with a turn-around time of a few days. In fact this is the only output that PSC mails to users. In this manner several minutes of animation can be produced, possibly spanning several individual animations, a night. Presently there are three parallel animation systems, two Umatics and one laser disk recorder.

Animation sequences

Cost savings

In addition to purely remote use, three of the heaviest animation users decided to purchase their own hardware, and used GPLOT software to produce their own animation systems. Since all necessary software was provided, the cost to these users was much less than a commercial system.

Random access

The size of the CGM files required for animations (frequently close to a gigabyte) motivated extension of the CGM standard to include a random access capability. This was done in cooperation with the SLATEC supercomputing community and it has worked very well to date.

The original GPLOT system was written entirely in the C programming language, compilable under either the UNIX or VMS operating systems. As the move began towards sophisticated graphical user interfaces and users began to request more capabilities for GPLOT (including on-screen animations for workstations) it was decided to completely rewrite GPLOT in an object-oriented fashion using the C++ language. This greatly simplified the addition of some features, including on-screen animations using the X-Window system and a Motif user interface.

Graphical user interface

Object oriented

Port to Apple Macintosh

This C++ version also simplified the port to the Apple Macintosh operating system. The great majority of the code is common with two Macintosh specific modules, one for the user interface and one for the Quickdraw imaging system.

The object-oriented design was also intended to allow the easy integration of all of GPLOT's capabilities into other packages. Work is underway to perform this in combination with a documentation system to allow true text-graphics integration in a single system.

Access to other packages

8.4.2 The DrawCGM Graphics Subroutine Library

During the development of GPLOT, it became necessary to generate CGM files for test purposes. A simple library called CGMGen was written to do this. It had the ability to produce indexed or direct color CGM files, the interface being set up so that a single call generally produced a single CGM element.

Test facilities

At the same time it was becoming obvious that graphics packages available then, like Disspla, DI-3000, and the NCAR Graphics Library, lacked features needed to do some of the graphics required in a supercomputing environment. In particular, it is very common for a supercomputer user to wish to produce a color image from a two-dimensional regular array of data. This is done simply by mapping the data into a range of integer values, and drawing the image using those values as indices into a color map. It was required to provide this functionality to the users in a simple way.

Graphics from supercomputers

This led to the development of the DrawCGM graphics library, which is particularly well suited to the generation of raster images. The package provides facilities for manipulating color maps, scaling and quantizing rasters of reals, and drawing multiple images within a single CGM frame. The ability to produce other CGM primitives was added, such as markers, lines, polygons, and text as well, because these functions were readily available in CGMGen. Utilities to easily draw color bars and labels were also included. Because the primary task of DrawCGM was to handle color mapped

Raster images

images, only the indexed color facilities in CGMGen
were used. DrawCGM is written in FORTRAN, while
CGMGen is written in C.

Eventually confidence in the interpretation of the CGM
standard increased so that support for the independent
CGM generator in CGMGen could be dropped. This CGM

Interface to GPLOT   generator was replaced with a direct interface to the GPLOT
device driver library, making it possible to use the
CGMGen interface to do graphics interactively on any device supported by GPLOT. Since GPLOT also supports device drivers which create binary or clear CGM, the ability
to produce metafiles from DrawCGM was not lost. Thus
DrawCGM became an interactive package, supporting a
wide range of devices.

DrawCGM and CGMGen are distributed with the
GPLOT library, and are now quite widely used. DrawCGM

Applications   has been particularly successful for producing animations,
for example of hydrodynamic systems. Users will preview
animations either interactively or via a CGM metafile and
GPLOT, and will pass a CGM file containing the entire animation for recording when their results are satisfactory.
DrawCGM provides the ability to have multiple images
with distinct color maps on screen simultaneously, which
can greatly improve the information content of this sort of
animation. The underlying CGMGen layer still supports
the ability to use direct color, so it has been used to interface
a number of 24-bit color applications to the GPLOT device
driver library.

One feature which DrawCGM does not currently support is the ability to have multiple output devices open simultaneously. It is hoped to correct this when CGMGen is
recoded to interface to the new object-oriented version of
GPLOT.

8.4.3 The P3D Three-Dimensional Metafile Project

Success with a metafile-based environment for 2D graphics led to the consideration of a similar system for three-dimensional models. The goal would be to produce a format which all programs generating 3D models at the PSC would produce, and which could be rendered in three dimensions on a wide variety of platforms. The existence of this format would allow models to be transferred between the central site and user sites, and would simplify the software support situation analogous to the simplification provided by CGM. This is not to belittle the importance of interactive 3D graphics; it is simply believed that a complete environment requires both interactive and metafile forms and that it is appropriate to investigate the metafile approach.

2D to 3D

Unfortunately, unlike the 2D case in which the standard CGM format already existed, there was and is no standard format for 3D scientific graphical models. The available non-standard formats were examined and none of them were found very satisfactory for current needs. Therefore a further format was developed, called P3D – the P denoting 'Programmable'.

Format for 3D

P3D is based on a subset of the Common Lisp language, with a small number of extensions to describe geometry. This makes P3D a complete programming language in itself, allowing it the same flexibility which programmability provides to the Postscript page description language. Like Postscript, it is never necessary for a user to actually write a program in P3D. A model generating program (for example a molecular modeler) produces a P3D model, and a P3D viewer translates the model into images which the user can view. The P3D viewer includes a locally written Lisp interpreter; there is no need for the site using P3D to license an interpreter from a third party. Because the full 3D structure of the model is stored in the P3D file, the model can be viewed from any direction or incorporated into more complex models.

3D language

Needs of scientific **P3D** was designed to support the needs of scientific visu-
visualization alization, rather than those of photorealism or, for example,
computer aided design. The current implementation sup-
ports ten geometrical primitives, fairly complete lighting
and camera information, arbitrary transformations, and a
very extensible attribute structure in a hierarchical model
environment.

Rendering options P3D models can be viewed on seven different renderers,
with more under development. These range from a simple
mouse-driven renderer for the X Window System environment to renderers for solid modeling workstations and a ray
tracer. A number of generators for P3D models now exist,
including translators for molecular dynamics output,
marching cubes algorithms, a general purpose subroutine library, and a simple tool for generating fly-bys of P3D models. The programmability of P3D makes it easy to modify
existing codes to produce models in P3D format, since the
metafile can essentially be tailored to the needs of the code
rather than the other way round.

Animation As with CGM, it is possible to produce animation from
a P3D model file in which a number of views are specified.
This allows animations to be previewed on a user's workstation, and then nicely rendered (possibly ray-traced) and recorded as high quality video animation. The animation system uses the same hardware and some of the same software
as the CGM-based system.

Exchange of 3D It would be useful for the P3D format to become a com-
model data mon medium of exchange for 3D models. There are currently about 40 sites on the mailing list of those using or inter-
ested in P3D, so some progress is being made toward this
goal. Current work is on designing interfaces which will allow general interactive visualization packages like Stardent's
AVS and the Ohio Supercomputer Center's apE to read and
write P3D models, and to incorporate additional renderer
interfaces such as Pixar's Renderman. Other development
projects include a translator to generate P3D from finite element models, and general modifications to improve the
functioning of the P3D renderers.

8.4.4 Software Availability

Software developed at the Pittsburgh Supercomputing Cen-   *Free of charge*
ter, including GPLOT, DrawCGM, and the P3D software
suite, is available free of charge by anonymous FTP from
the machine ftp.psc.edu. DrawCGM is included in the
GPLOT package; the P3D software is a separate distribution
but (depending on the configuration chosen) may require
the GPLOT software. If you take GPLOT, please send mail
to Anjana Kar (kar@psc.edu) to be added to the appropriate
mailing list. Advanced questions regarding GPLOT, as op-   *Information*
posed to simply taking and installing the software, can be
directed to Phil Andrews (andrews@psc.edu). If you take
P3D, please send mail to Joel Welling (welling@psc.edu) to
be added to that mailing list.

Contributed by Joel Welling and Phil Andrews.

Further information from:

Dr. Joel Welling
Pittsburgh Supercomputer Center
4400 Fifth Avenue
Pittsburgh, PA 15213, U.S.A.
Tel: 412-268-6352
Email: welling@psc.edu

8.5 RAYSHADE

This is an excellent ray-tracing program for scene rendering.   *Scene rendering*
It handles many different kinds of object. It is available from
the University of Yale and the University of Utah.

   Rayshade reads a multi-line ASCII file describing a scene   *Format*
to be rendered and produces a Utah Raster RLE format file
of the raytraced image.

Facilities   Features include:

- Primitives:
  boxes
  cones
  cylinders
  height fields
  planes
  polygons
  spheres
  triangles (flat- or Phong-shaded),
- Composite objects,
- Point, directional, and extended (area) light sources,
- Solid texturing and bump mapping of primitives, objects, and individual instances of objects,
- Antialiasing through adaptive supersampling or "jittered" sampling,
- Arbitrary linear transformations of primitives, instances of objects, and texture/bump maps,
- Use of uniform spatial subdivision and/or hierarchy of bounding volumes to speed rendering,
- Options to facilitate rendering of stereo pairs,
- Support for the Linda parallel programming language.

An awk script is provided to translate NFF format scripts to rayshade format.

C language   Rayshade is written in C with parsing support provided through lex and yacc. The C, lex and yacc files comprise approximately 8000 lines of code. Sites without lex and yacc can make use of the C source files produced by lex and yacc which are included in this distribution.

Platforms   Rayshade has been tested on a number of UNIX-based machines, including Vaxes, Sun Workstations, Iris 4D Workstations, Encore Multimax, AT&T 3B2/310, CRAY XMP, and IBM RTs. In addition, support is provided for the Amiga using the Aztec C compiler.

Getting a copy   Rayshade makes use of the Utah Raster toolkit, a package consisting of a large number of useful image manipulation programs, test images, and a library to read and write images written using the toolkit's RLE format. The toolkit is available via anonymous FTP from cs.utah.edu or from weedeater.math.yale.edu.

Those sites that cannot or do not want to use the Utah Raster toolkit can make use of a compile-time option to produce images written using a generic file format identical to that used in Mark Van de Wettering's "MTV" raytracer.

Rayshade is copyrighted in a "Gnu-like" manner.

Rayshade is available via anonymous ftp from weedeater.math.yale.edu (192.26.88.42) in pub/Rayshade.2.21.tar.Z. The Utah Raster toolkit is available in pub/UtahToolkit.tar.Z.

8.6 NASA Ames Software

8.6.1 PLOT3D

PLOT3D is a computer graphics program designed to visualize the grids and solutions of computational fluid dynamics. Eighty-five functions are available, and versions are available for many systems. PLOT3D can handle multiple grids with many grid points, and can produce varieties of model renderings, such as wireframe or flat shaded. Output from PLOT3D can be used in animation programs.

Computational fluid dynamics

PLOT3D User's Manual and PLOT3D software can be distributed free of charge and without copyright to any institution or business in the USA.

Availability

Contact:

Workstation Applications Office
NASA Ames Research Center, MS258-2
Moffett Field, CA 94035, U.S.A.

8.6.2 SURF

A further program, SURF, allows the user to input PLOT3D grid and solution files and interactively create wireframe, shaded, and function mapped parts to view, and

Interactive viewing of PLOT3D files

then output to ARCGraph files which can be animated using the Graphics Animation System (GAS). Shaded parts are created based on user specified lightsources (at least 20), viewpoint, and the ambient light level. The function mapped parts can have their color spectrum adjusted interactively. Legends can be created to show the correlation of color and normalised function values (i.e., pressure, density, temperature, and mach number). Also, function-mapped parts can be clipped so that they only show contours within a specified range of function values (e.g., normalised pressure between 1 and 2).

Further facilities   Other features of SURF include the ability to work with several grids and solutions, grid/solution deletion, support of multi-grid files, input/output for colormaps, matrices, light sources, function extrema, screen dump pixel input/output, display of current grid and part attribute data, and a UNIX shell escape.

8.6.3 Graphics Animation System (GAS)

Animation system   GAS is a graphics animation software system that is menu-driven and provides fast, simple viewing capability as well as more complex rendering and animation features. It is used to display two- and three-dimensional objects along with computed data, and also to record animation sequences on video digital disks, videotape, and 16 mm film.

8.6.4 Applications in Computational Fluid Dynamics (CFD)

Illustrations of use   Some example applications have been the following: pressure distribution inside the space shuttle main engine, vortex flows over the wing/strake surface of F-16 aircraft, pressure distribution on an oscillating F-5 wing, simulation of turbine engine rotor-stator interaction, particle traces over the space shuttle orbiter, and pressure distributions over the high-speed National Aerospace Plane.

Getting a solution   The CFD software analysis cycle begins with the design of a test geometry 'grid' (e.g., forward-swept wing model with surrounding airspace), specification of simulation conditions (e.g., angle of attack, mach number, reynolds number) and coding and execution on supercomputers of 'flow solver' programs that solve the higher-order mathematical equations governing the flight characteristics. Then the numerical solution data is collected and converted to graphics images of fluid flows, pressure distributions, shock waves, and particle traces using workstations running PLOT3D and other specialised graphics programs. Then SURF can be used to add shading/coloring enhancements to the images. Finally, animation sequences are generated and recorded with GAS.

Use of computer graphics

Animation

The results produced are animated 16 mm films and videotapes showing solid, pressure mapped aircraft models with wing/body vortices, particle traces, temperature distributions and shock waves. The ability to display the physical properties in aerodynamic flight is a tremendous aid in understanding and designing aircraft geometries for specific flight characteristics. By using interactive computer graphics in the aerodynamics study, the critical areas (e.g., high turbulence, high temperature, reverse flow) immediately become obvious so they can be studied more closely using a finer grid, more particle traces, and higher-resolution mapping of pressure or temperature contours. For example, graphical studies revealed high turbulence and pressure inside the Space Shuttle Orbiter main engine hot gas manifold, and further analysis led to a redesign of the engine with reduced decisions internal pressure and turbulence.

Visualization aids understanding

Studying physical properties

Design decisions

(Courtesy of PLOT3D User's Manual by P. P. Walatka and P. G. Buning, SURF User's Guide by T. Plessel, and GAS User's Manual by T. Plessel).

Contact:

NASA Ames Research Center
Mail Stop 258-2
Moffett Field, CA 94035, U.S.A.
Tel: 415-694-4052

8.7 IRISPLOT

Display of surfaces   IRISPLOT is an extended version of GNUplot for the Silicon Graphics workstation that allows algebraic surfaces to be displayed, shaded, etc.

IRISPLOT allows the user to define some of the graphical objects built from surfaces and curves, which in turn are defined from mathematical functions, discrete maps, differential equations and data files. The user has full control of *Viewing the* the graphical attributes, which includes viewing, orthogonal *surface* or perspective projection, object transformation, object slicing, 8 different light sources with different color and location, and different material properties for each object in plot. It also allows contouring on the surfaces.

For more information, contact system@math.arizona.edu

8.8 ISVAS

Interactive FhG-AGD in Darmstadt provides a tool called ISVAS, an in-*visualization* teractive volume visualizer for SUN (X11/OSF Motif) and SGI (GL/Motif). ISVAS stands for Interactive Software for Visual AnalysiS of fracture mechanics. The system has been developed for the visualization of the results of three-dimensional finite element simulations in fracture mechanics and other application areas.

Finite element The main aim in the development of ISVAS is interacti-*data* vity. Finite element analysis produces large amounts of data and the graphical presentation of the data is a computer-intensive process. Therefore there is a need for presenting data at speed, but with low amounts of detail. The tools allow a rough preview of the data and interactive specification of parameters, such as viewpoint and cut planes. The user can thus produce a quick picture of what the data looks like, specify the parameters of the required image, then render it for a higher-quality presentation.

The X11 version, which is running on SUN, DEC, and other machines, has already been installed at the Technical University of Munich, the University of Lisbon, and the University of Mexico. Sun (SPARC) code is available, and also source code of the data filters for adaption to the user's own volume data. Data filters for several FE-data types are provided. Version 1.2 of ISVAS allows the user to visualize scalar volume data. The next version will also allow vector data to be displayed.

ISVAS is built upon X Windows and OSF/Motif toolkit *Portability* to be portable to any UNIX colour workstation.

Further information:

Dr. Martin Goebel
Fraunhofer-Arbeitsgruppe
für Graphische Datenverarbeitung
Wilhelminenstrasse 7
W-6100 Darmstadt
Federal Republic of Germany
Tel: 49-6151-155123
Fax: 49-6151-155199
Email: goebel@de.fhg.agd

Chapter 9
Other Uses of Visualization Tools

9.1 Art and Design

Creative and artistic applications

Tools such as those described in this guide can be also used by those whose primary interest is not in the scientific content of the information presented, but rather the creative or aesthetic value.

Barlow et al. (1990) outlines how artists create effects and explores issues at the interface between art and science.

Artists and designers

Artists and sculptors have been using computer-assisted tools for a number of years (Lansdown, 1989) and these tools often promote new and unexpected ways of creating and developing images and objects. Architects, designers and engineers also use these methods. Thus visualization tools are not confined to scientific visualization but can be used in all areas where the user is seeking to create and manipulate information via visual means.

9.2 The 5th Dimension Animation System

3D animation and visualization

The 5th Dimension Project is a large research project in three-dimensional animation and visualization. The main objective of the project is the animation of synthetic actors in their environment, which involves a number of related areas of computer animation and scientific visualization. In

Applications

particular, the following applications are being developed:

- animation of articulated bodies based on mechanical laws,
- vision-based behavioural animation,

- hair rendering and animation,
- object grasping,
- facial animation,
- personification in walking models,
- synchronization in task-level animation,
- deformation of flexible and elastic objects,
- cloth animation with detection of collision.

To coordinate efforts and allow good communication between the various applications, a toolkit of high-level dynamic classes, both two- and three-dimensional, has been constructed. This toolkit, called the 5th Dimension Toolkit, uses a uniformly object-oriented design for all its data structures, resulting in a high degree of integration between various applications.

High-level toolkit

Object oriented

The 5th Dimension animation system is intended to offer to the animator a full 3D interaction including the possibility of entering into the virtual world and communicating with the synthetic actors. The hardware used consists of 21 Silicon Graphics IRIS Workstations including three Powervision (VGX) models. Most 5th Dimension applications take advantage of visual 3D interfaces using the various 3D devices available in the laboratories: two datagloves, several SpaceBalls, an EyePhone, a 3-D Polhemus digitizer, a Live Video Digitizer, a StereoView station, and a synthesizer keyboard controlled by a NeXT Cube workstation.

3D interaction

Virtual worlds

In the current version, six applications provide a user interface based on 3D devices:

3D devices

- the sculpting program SURFMAN,
- the Muscle and Expression editor in the SMILE Facial Animation system,
- the cloth design software,
- the hand gesture recording system GESTURE LAB,
- the program to create 3D paths for cameras, objects and light sources,
- a communication program animator-actor (in development).

3D input The first three programs are mainly based on the ball and mouse metaphor. SURFMAN may also take advantage of StereoView and the 3D Polhemus digitizer. Hand gestures are recorded using the DataGlove and 3D paths are mainly generated using the SpaceBall. We are developing a way of creating camera paths based on the EyePhone. The communication program animator-actor uses the Living Video Digitizer to capture the animator face.

Other applications in the 5th Dimension system are only based on mouse interaction. They include:

- an interactive system to design individual walking,
- the BODY-MOVING human keyframe animation system,
- a hair modelling and rendering program.

Submitted by Nadia Magnenat Thalmann, University of Geneva, and Daniel Thalmann, Swiss Federal Institute of Technology.

Fig. 9.1
Cloth Animation

Figure 9.1 shows cloth animation from the film Flashback, by B. Lafleur, N.M. and D. Thalmann, University of Geneva and Swiss Federal Institute of Technology.

Fig. 9.2
Human Walking

Frame from the film Still Walking by A. Paouri, R. Boulic, N. M. and D. Thalmann, University of Geneva and Swiss Federal Institute of Technology.

Fig. 9.3
Hair Rendering

Hair rendering by A. LeBlanc, A. Paouri, N.M. and D. Thalmann, University of Geneva and Swiss Federal Institute of Technology.

9.3 Multimedia Environments

Project KICK

Multi-media KICK is an interactive multimedia environment designed to support industrial training applications (Serra et al. 1991). The main component of KICK is an authoring environment for the designers to organize the contents and orchestrate the presentation of multimedia information. The medium types supported include text, image, 3D graphics, and video.

Hierarchy The effective organization of multimedia information for interactive access is of major concern. In KICK, multimedia information is organized primarily using the natural hierarchy of the physical objects to be modeled. In order to permit associative access to information as advocated in hypermedia, auxiliary access paths are provided by means of other media, such as text, image, and video. The resulting information structure thus facilitates both structured and associative access to information.

In KICK, the same direct manipulation interface is used to manipulate information of any medium type. To achieve *Video and image* this for video and image media, techniques have been developed to allow the synchronization of 3D graphics models and animation of video sequences and images. In addition, techniques to model object motions, constraints and relationships have also been developed.

Training The system developed is intended for training applications, where users can learn about the structure and operations of a complex mechanism by interactively:

- accessing its component hierarchy,
- experimenting with how various components interact with each other in dynamic operating conditions,
- studying the effects of various externally applied forces on different parts of the mechanism.

Examples To demonstrate the usability of system KICK, two applications for industrial training have been developed. One is based on an aircraft and the other on a 1/8 scale model car with a 0.21 cc engine. Figure 9.4 shows an engine component of the aircraft application in four different media – 3D graphics, text, video and image. Figure 9.5 shows the engine component of the model car application. Through the display, the user may interact with any medium type to retrieve further information or to view the operations of the engine in context.

KICK is developed on a Silicon 4D/210 GTX workstation with a Live Video Digitizer. The video input is obtained from a Sony LDP-1500 laser disk player. KICK is implemented using Starship, a frame language developed at ISS (Loo 1991).

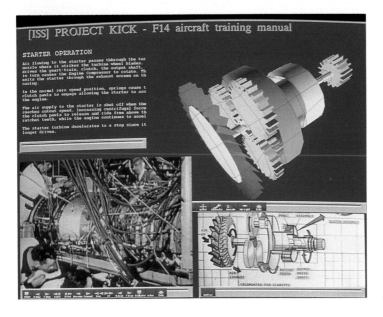

Fig. 9.4
Turbine Engine
from Aircraft
Application

The figure shows the concept of a turbine engine in four different media – 3D graphics (top right), text (top left), video (bottom right) and image (bottom left). Users may interact directly with any medium type to retrieve further information about its subcomponents, view the video about the assembly of the engine, or generate an animation of a 3D model.

Fig. 9.5
Concept Engine
from Car
Application

This figure shows the interface of KICK without the video window. The users may again interact with any medium type directly to obtain further information.

References

Loo J. P. L. (1991) The Starship Manual (Version 2.0), ISS Internal Technical Report, TR91-54-1

Serra, L., Chua, T. S. and Teh, W. S. (1991) A Model for Integrating Multimedia Information around 3D Graphics Hierarchies. The Visual Computer (in press)

Information supplied by Luis Serra and Wei-Shoong Teh, Institute of Systems Science, National University of Singapore, and Tat-Seng Chua, Department of Information Systems and Computer Science, National University of Singapore.

Chapter 10
Conclusions

10.1 Strategic Importance
of Scientific Visualization

In view of the believed strategic importance of scientific visualization it is timely to consider what tools and techniques should be provided in this area for the community,
and also what kind of initiatives and objectives should be
supported and promoted.

Tools and techniques needed

It is important that scientific visualization be developed
and promoted. Here are some of the strategic issues that
need addressing if scientific visualization tools are to be effectively utilised.

Promotion

Forum for:
- Planning, discussion, and problem-solving,
- Coordinate developments that may be required in the area,
- Exchange experiences in different application areas,
- Share common software tools, where available,
- Disseminate information,
- Assist with teaching materials,
- Education and training issues.

Plan for:
- Any new products that may be needed,
- Any general network developments that may be needed,
- Any general video facilities that may be needed,
- Providing visualization tools for the community,
- Supporting research into scientific visualization.

10.2 Current Developments

*More detailed
modeling*

These advances will allow mathematical models and simulations to become increasingly complex and detailed. This results in a closer approximation to reality, thus enhancing the possibility of acquiring new knowledge and understanding. Scientific visualization is concerned with methods of understanding large collections of numerical values containing a great deal of information. The scientist has to be able to make effective use of this information for analytic purposes.

*Interactive
3D design*

A further aspect is that increases in computer performance allow 3D problems in simulation and design to be done interactively. In addition, processes that formerly separated out simulation and design can now bring them together (e.g., in CAD, or in the design of new drugs). This in turn moves the user into a new era of methods of design.

*Handling multi-
dimensional data*

Control over fine simulations, interactivity, and computer performance mean that vast amounts of multidimensional data can be generated. Superworkstations allow this data to be displayed in optimum ways. These features and capabilities are driving the current wave of interest in scientific visualization.

*New techniques
for analysis*

Work is proceeding in evolving new techniques for data display as the data is being analysed.

10.3 More User-Friendly Facilities

*What you drive is
what you see
(WYDIWYS)*

A further current trend is to make software tools for visualization more user-friendly and accessible to a wide variety of application areas, thus increasing their potential and usability.

Improvements to the graphical user interface and the way the user interacts with the model are likely to provide more effective ways of communicating relationships and other aspects of data to the user.

10.4 Further Information

The book by Nielson et al. (1990) contains a wide variety *Applications* of current applications of scientific visualization and also an excellent bibliography of scientific papers. A 2-hour video tape is available with the book. This tape gives effective demonstrations of the projects described in the book. The format is NTSC but can be played on a dual-format player (such as Panasonic J35) in the UK without any problem. This player can take both PAL and NTSC formats.

Frenkel (1988) provides a general introduction to basic *Introduction* visualization techniques.

Thalmann (1990) contains a number of papers in the areas of scientific visualization and graphical simulation.

For further details of any of the software mentioned earlier, please contact the local office of the vendor. In addition, Chapter 11 contains a list of references which may be of further interest.

There are numerous electronic mail subscription lists and bulletin boards on topics in scientific visualization and also on specific items of software.

10.5 What to do next?

The majority of users have some experience of tools for pre- *Understanding* sentation graphics. Some users are currently using visualiza- *data* tion tools of one kind or another, in that the use of such tools facilitates the process of understanding more about the data. However, very few users have access to visualization systems of the kind described in this guide. It is expected that access to such systems will become more common as costs decrease and experience in application areas increases.

The developments in the U.S.A. outlined in Chapter 6 indicate the trends as of 1991, of course!

A more detailed reference volume on scientific visualization is available entitled *Scientific Visualization – Techniques and Applications* edited by Brodlie et al., Springer-Verlag, 1991.

References

H. Barlow, C. Blakemore, M. Weston-Smith (eds.): Images and Understanding: Thoughts about Images, Ideas and Understanding. Cambridge University Press, 1990

Outlines how artists create effects and explores issues at the interface between art and science.

K. W. Brodlie, L. A. Carpenter, R. A. Earnshaw, J. R. Gallop, R. J. Hubbold, A. M. Mumford, C. D. Osland, P. Quarendon (eds.): Scientific Visualization – Techniques and Applications. Springer-Verlag, 1991

This volume represents a full consideration of the subject of scientific visualization and is intended to be a reference guide for the community on the technical aspects of the subject. The topics covered include: the framework, visualization techniques, data facilities, human computer interface, applications, products, a glossary of terms, enabling technologies, and an extensive bibliography.

D. Scott Dyer: A Dataflow Toolkit for Visualization. IEEE Computer Graphics and Applications, 10:4, 60–69 (July 1990)

This article describes the design principles behind the apE visualization software (apE stands for Animation Production Environment).

E. J. Farrell (ed.): Visual Interpretation of Complex Data. IBM Journal of Research and Development, 35:1/2 (Jan-March 1991)

A special issue of the IBM Journal of Research and Development on visualization. There are papers on visualization of volumetric data, image display and interpretation, and animation for data interpretation. There is also a companion video "Understanding Complex Data with Computer Animation".

K. A. Frenkel: The Art and Science of Visualizing Data. Communications of the ACM, 31:2, 110–121 (1988)

An introductory paper which looks at a range of application areas and the uses of visualization tools and techniques. A wide range of pictures illustrate some of the techniques currently being used.

K. A. Frenkel: Volume Rendering. Communications of the ACM, 32:4, 426–435 (1989)

Outline of volume visualization, with application areas.

A. Kaufman (ed.): Volume Visualisation. IEEE Press, 1990

A collection of most of the key papers in the area of volume visualization.

R. J. Lansdown, R. A. Earnshaw (eds.): Computers in Art, Design and Animation. Springer-Verlag, 1989

Collection of papers on the area of creative uses of computer graphics and associated tools and techniques.

B. H. McCormick, T. A. DeFanti, M. D. Brown (eds.): Visualization in Scientific Computing. ACM SIGGRAPH Computer Graphics, 21:6 (November 1987)

The original Panel Report which outlines the political, economic, educational, and technological aspects of scientific visualization as an emerging discipline.

B. H. McCormick, T. A. DeFanti, M. D. Brown (eds.): Visualization in Scientific Computing. IEEE Computer, 23:8 (August 1989)

An updated version of the original McCormick (1987) report, outlining current progress and advances in scientific visualization.

G. M. Nielson, B. Shriver, L. Rosenblum (eds.): Visualization in Scientific Computing. IEEE Press, 1990

A collection of papers in the areas of techniques and applications of scientific visualization from a variety of academic, government, and industrial organisations in the USA.

N. M. Patrikalakis (ed.): Scientific Visualization of Physical Phenomena. Springer-Verlag, 1991

Proceedings of the 9th International Conference of the Computer Graphics Society on the theme of scientific visualization. This volume contains a number of key invited papers in the areas of applications of scientific visualization, including engineering design, spacecraft exploration of the solar system, and remote subsea exploration.

D. Thalmann (ed.): Scientific Visualisation and Graphics Simulation. Wiley, 1990

Computational and graphical techniques that are necessary to visualize scientific experiments are surveyed in this volume, with a number of case studies in particular application areas.

N. Magnenat-Thalmann, D. Thalmann (eds.): New Trends in Animation and Visualization. Wiley, 1991

A collection of papers covering state-of-the-art topics in the areas of scientific visualization, animation, graphical simulation, modeling, hypermedia, facial animation, natural phenomena, human modeling, and applications.

E. R. Tufte: The Visual Display of Quantitative Information. Graphics Press, USA, 1983

E. R. Tufte: Envisioning Information. Graphics Press, USA, 1990

Two introductory texts with guidelines on displaying information effectively.

C. Upson, T. Faulhaber, D. Kamins, D. Laidlaw, D. Schlegel, J. Vroom, R. Gurwitz, A. van Dam: The Application Visualization System: A Computational Environment for Scientific Visualization. IEEE Computer Graphics and Applications, 9:4, 30–42 (1989)

This paper describes the design principles of AVS.

C. Upson: Volumetric Visualization Techniques. In: D. F. Rogers, R. A. Earnshaw (eds): State of the Art in Computer Graphics – Visualization and Modeling. Springer-Verlag, 1991

Description of volumetric techniques from one of the designers of AVS and the designer of Explorer.

Sources of Figures

Rendered by DESIGNBASE	Figure 7.27
Reproduced by permission of Dynamics Graphics Ltd.	Figure 7.20, −7.24
Reproduced by permission © IBM UK Scientific Centre	Figure 2.7, 3.3
Reproduced by permission © LightWork Design Ltd.	Figure 7.25, 7.26
Reproduced by permission © Precison Visuals Ltd.	Figure 3.10, 7.6, 7.7
Reproduced by permission © Regional Geophysics Research Group, British Geological Survey	Figure 3.5
Reproduced by permission Ricoh Company Ltd.	Figure 7.27, 7.28, 7.29, 7.31
Reproduced by permission © David F. Rogers, 1991	Figure 2.11−2.13
Reproduced by permission of Stardent Computer Ltd.	Figure 3.12
© 1990 SUN Microsystems, Inc. Rendered on a SUN SPARCstation 470VX + MVX	Figure 7.14
© 1990 SUN Microsystems, Inc. Rendered on a SUN SPARCstation using SunVision software	Figure 7.15, 7.17−7.19
©SUN Microsystems, Inc. Rendered on a SUN SPARCstation VX+MVX using Westover's splat software	Figure 7.16
Data courtesy of Frank Bryan at NCAR	Figure 8.8

Courtesy of Dr. B. El-Haddadeh, University of Leeds, and UNIRAS software	Figure 3.9
Courtesy of Todd Elvins, San Diego Supercomputer Center (SDSC); Data: Mark Ellisman, University of California, San Diego; Visualization: Dave Hessler, SDSC; Software: SYNU from SDSC	Figure 3.11
Courtesy of Todd Elvins, San Diego Supercomputer Center (SDSC); Data: Ted Cranford, University of California, Santa Cruz; Visualization: Todd Elvins, Phil Mercurio, SDSC, Software: SUN Microsystems Voxvu	Figure 3.13
Courtesy of Prof. Elliot K. Fishman MD	Figure 2.8
Courtesy of Prof. T.L. Kunii	Figure 2.14, 2.15
Courtesy of the Lamont Doherty Geologic Observatory	Figure 7.21
Courtesy of the Lawrence Livermore National Laboratory	Figure 7.20
Courtesy of Silicon Graphics Ltd.	Figure 7.11–7.13
Courtesy of Simultec, Switzerland	Figure 7.22
Data courtesy of Dr. Michael Torello	Figure 8.7
Courtesy of Craig Upson	Figure 2.1, 3.1, 3.2, 3.4
Reproduced by permission © Nadia M. Thalman, D. Thalman, 1991	Figure 9.1–9.3
Reproduced by permission of ©U.K. Meteorological Office	Figure 2.4–2.6
Reproduced by permission of © UNIRAS Ltd.	Figure 7.4, 7.5
Reproduced by permission of © Wavefront Technologies Ltd.	Figure 3.6–3.8, 7.1–7.3
Courtesy of Geoff Wyvill & Brian Wyvill	Figure 2.9, 2.10

Printing: Saladruck, Berlin
Binding: Buchbinderei Lüderitz & Bauer, Berlin